MUSIC ★ FOR

ABC MUSIC SERIES

★ BOOK THREE ★

★ YOUNG ★ AMERICANS

RICHARD C. BERG
DIRECTOR OF MUSIC EDUCATION, YONKERS, N. Y.

DANIEL S. HOOLEY
ASSOCIATE PROFESSOR OF MUSIC EDUCATION
GEORGIA TEACHERS COLLEGE, COLLEGEBORO, GEORGIA

ROBERT PACE
ASSOCIATE PROFESSOR OF MUSIC EDUCATION
COLUMBIA UNIVERSITY, TEACHERS COLLEGE, NEW YORK CITY

JOSEPHINE WOLVERTON
ASSISTANT SUPERVISOR OF MUSIC, EVANSTON PUBLIC SCHOOLS
AND ASSISTANT PROFESSOR OF MUSIC
NORTHWESTERN UNIVERSITY, EVANSTON, ILLINOIS

CLAUDEANE BURNS
CONSULTANT, AMERICAN BOOK COMPANY, CHICAGO, ILLINOIS

AMERICAN BOOK COMPANY ©

Grateful acknowledgment is made to the following publishers and authors for permission
to reprint material used in this book:

Elizabeth Newell and *Child Life:* For "I'm a Goose."

Ilo Orleans: For his poem "Song of Coiors."

Mabel Watts and *Piggity's Magazine:* For "Peek-a-Boo Kangaroo."

Illustrations by Ezra Jack Keats and Brinton Turkle

E. P. 5

CONTENTS

We Sing, Play, and Dance PAGES 108—131

We Listen and Hear PAGES 132—140

From Spring to Summer PAGES 141—171

Song Stories PAGES 172—191

Indexes PAGES 192—199

Singing Along

Traditional Rhyme   Music by Daniel Hooley

LAZILY

As I was go-ing a-long, a-long,

A-sing-ing a com-i-cal song, a song,

The road that I trav-'led was long, long, long!

And so I just went a-sing-ing a-long,

Sing-ing a-long, a-long.

Sometimes, when you are going along, you may be "A-humming a comical song, a song" or "A-whistling a comical song, a song."

1

Starting the Day

Adapted Words   Czech Folk Tune

1. Let's sing a bright mel-o-dy, one just as gay as can be,
Let's sing a bright mel-o-dy to start the day;
Is-n't it pleas-ant to sing, au-tumn and win-ter or spring?
Just sing a bright mel-o-dy to start the day.

2. Let's play a bright melody, one just as gay as can be,
Let's play a bright melody to start the day;
Isn't it pleasant to hear, through all the months of the year,
Songs that we learn how to play to start the day?

3. Let's dance a bright melody, one just as gay as can be,
Let's dance a bright melody to start the day;
Isn't it pleasant to swing 'round and about in a ring?
Just dance a bright melody to start the day.

Painting

Words and Music by Stephen Scott

BRIGHTLY

3/4

1. I like to paint with blues and greens,
2. I like to paint with pinks and grays,

I like to paint with reds.____
I like to paint with browns.____

I like to paint pic-tures of planes and ships
I like to paint pic-tures of cars and trains

And hous-es and gar-den beds.____
And peo-ple and coun-try towns.____

3

Our Classroom

Words by Rebecca Stevens Music by Cecilia Johns

QUICKLY

Our class-room is a place for us to work and play and share,

Our teach-er helps us learn to use our books and pen-cils there;

We sing a song and play a game or paint and work with clay;

Our class-room is a home for us, we live there ev - 'ry day.

4

Old John Braddledum

Adapted Words   English Folk Tune

WITH HUMOR

1. Hi there, One, Hi there, One, Now my song has just be-gun,— With a rum-tum tad-dle-dum, Old John Brad-dle-dum, Hey, how sil-ly can you be?

2. Hey there, Two, Hey there, Two, Ev'ry foot should wear a shoe.
With a rumtum taddledum, Old John Braddledum,
Hey, how silly can you be?

3. Hey there, Three, Hey there, Three, Some like coffee, some like tea.
With a rumtum taddledum, Old John Braddledum,
Hey, how silly can you be?

4. Hey there, Four, Hey there, Four, Take the doorknob from the door.
With a rumtum taddledum, Old John Braddledum,
Hey, how silly can you be?

On the second and third phrases, Classmate One claps, makes up
a little dance, or does anything he chooses to do as the class sings.
He is followed by Classmate Two, and so on.

Make up some more verses.

5

Ta-ra-ra Boom-de-ay

Adapted from an old song

A sil - ly song I heard to - day,

The mel - o - dy was bright and gay;

Clev-er lit-tle catch-y tune, I could sing it night or noon:

6

Ta-ra-ra boom-de-ay, ── Ta-ra-ra boom-de-ay, ──

Ta-ra-ra boom-de-ay, ── Ta-ra-ra boom-de-ay, ──

Ta-ra-ra boom-de-ay, ── Ta-ra-ra boom-de-ay, ──

Ta-ra-ra boom-de-ay, ── Ta-ra-ra boom-de-ay. ── Boom!
(Spoken)

7

Where will you sing louder? Where will you sing softer?

Autumn Bonfires

Words and Music by Stephen Scott

WITH EXPRESSION

Crack-ling, crack-ling flames are reach-ing high,

Reach-ing, reach-ing   up-ward to the sky,

Flames leap up   and then sink down,

Then the bon-fire   dies up-on the ground.

Find a little tune that goes like this: ⌃

Song of Colors

Words by Ilo Orleans   Music by Robert Pace

There's a black, black crow on the brown, brown tree;

There's a gray, gray ship on the dark, dark sea;

There's a white, white horse on the green, green hill;

There's a red, red bow on the bright, bright Jill;

There's a yel-low, yel-low moon in the blue, blue sky;

There's a pur-ple, pur-ple plum in a yum-yum pie!

Pop! Goes the Weasel

Traditional American Song

IN A LIVELY MANNER

1. __ All a-round the chick-en coop
2. A pen-ny for a spool_of thread,

The mon-key chased the wea-sel,
A pen-ny for a nee-dle,

That's the way the mon-ey goes,
That's the way the mon-ey goes,

Pop! goes the wea - sel.
Pop! goes the wea - sel.

I've no time to wait or sigh, No time to whee-dle,

On-ly time to say good-by, Pop! goes the wea-sel!

Seesaw

Up and down,
Up and down,
Seesaws pop up,
Seesaws drop down.

The down is a bump,
The up is a jump.
Seesaw, seesaw,
Up!

   —Evelyn Beyer

Think of a good tune for this poem. You can make it go up and down.
The words tell you how the tune should go. Make seesaws as you sing.

Do as I'm Doing

Folk Style

IN STRICT RHYTHM

1. Do as I'm do-ing, Fol-low, fol-low me!

Do as I'm do-ing, Fol-low, fol-low me!

End

Go to the beginning.

If I do it high or low, If I do it fast or slow,

2. Clap as I'm clapping, Follow, follow me!
3. Play as I'm playing, Follow, follow me!

You can sing about walking, skipping, jumping, or whatever you please.

Muskrat, Muskrat

Kentucky Folk Song

LIVELY

1. Musk-rat, Musk-rat! What makes your coat so brown?

"Been liv-ing in the wa-ter all my life;

12

It's a won - der I don't drown."

Refrain

Sing hey did-dle dum -a, sing hey did-dle dum-a,

Sing hey did-dle dum-a dee; Sing hey did-dle dum-a,

Sing hey did-dle dum-a, Musk-rat's life for me!

2. Rabbit, Rabbit! What makes your tail so white?
"Well, ev'rybody on the mountain knows
That we had a snow last night."
Sing hey diddle duma, Sing hey diddle duma,
Sing hey diddle duma dee;
Sing hey diddle duma, Sing hey diddle duma,
Rabbit's life for me!

Clap when you sing the Refrain, or play it on rhythm instruments.

13

What phrases have the highest notes?
What phrase has the lowest note?

Don't Go Near the Water

Adapted Words   American Folk Song

WITH MOTION

1. "Moth-er, may I   go out to swim?"

"Yes, my dar-ling daugh-ter;—

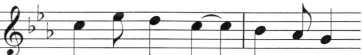

Hang your clothes on a hick-'ry limb

But don't go near the wa-ter."—

2. "Mother, may I go out to sail?"
   "Yes, my darling daughter;
   You may ride on a fish's tail,
   But don't go near the water."

3. "Mother, may I go out to fish?"
   "Yes, my darling daughter;
   You may catch one in a dish,
   But don't go near the water."

14

What words have this line pattern?

Sailing

Words and Music by Godfrey Marks

Sail - ing, sail - ing o - ver the bound-ing main,—
For man - y a storm - y wind shall blow
Ere Jack comes home a - gain; ——
Sail - ing, sail - ing o - ver the bound-ing main,—
For man - y a storm - y wind shall blow
Ere Jack comes home a - gain. ——

15

Captain Columbus

Adapted Words   Sailor Chantey

STURDILY

1. Cap-tain Co-lum-bus sailed from Spain,

With a   Yo! Heave!   Ho!

And he sailed a-long thro' the sun and rain,

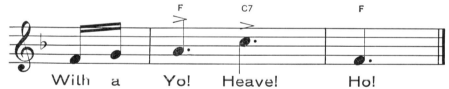

With a   Yo! Heave!   Ho!

2. He had a crew of frightened men,
   With a Yo! Heave! Ho!
   And they said: "Let's all turn back home again."
   With a Yo! Heave! Ho!

3. "Sail on and on!" was his command,
   With a Yo! Heave! Ho!
   And one day he sighted a shore and land,
   With a Yo! Heave! Ho!

4. October twelfth, Columbus Day,
   With a Yo! Heave! Ho!
   We all raise our flag and great honors pay,
   With a Yo! Heave! Ho!

16

●At Twilight

Adapted Words   Music by L. Waldmann

SLOWLY, WITH A GENTLE ROCKING MOTION

When the day is dy - ing, Birds are home - ward fly - ing,

Soon the sky is all a - glow, Twin-kling stars be-gin to show;

Lights be - low are beam - ing, Through the dark-ness gleam-ing;

Rest and peace now come to all, When the shad-ows fall.___

There is a curved line over each phrase. It shows the length
of the phrase. As you sing, make curved lines in the air
with your arms moving from side to side for each phrase.

There are many tunes that go down and up in this song.

17

Walking Alone

Words by Dorothy Aldis
Music by Anthony Burke

A SLOW WALK, ONE STEP TO EACH MEASURE

When you are walk-ing by your-self,

Here's some-thing nice to do:___

Kick a lit-tle stone and watch it

Hop a-head of you.___

The lit-tle stone is round and white,

Its shad-ow round and blue;___

A - long the side-walk, o - ver the cracks

The shad-ow bounc-es too. ___

Gnomes

Words by Julie Gibault   Music by Nancy Hoover

MYSTERIOUSLY

1.   I   like sto - ry-books that tell of mag - ic lit - tle men
2. "Gnomes" we call these lit - tle men that live be-yond the hill;

Who laugh and dance and play at night till morn-ing comes a-gain.
You nev - er   see them, day   or night, but hear them when it's still.

What kinds of notes and rests are there in this song?

Last Night

Paraphrase   Music by Halfdan Kjerulf

MODERATELY FAST

Last night the mock - ing bird woke me,

Last night when all was still; ____

It sang in the gold - en moon - light,

From out ＿＿＿＿＿ the wood - land hill.

I o - pened my win-dow＿ so＿ gen - tly,

The trees were all green and gold,＿＿

And oh!＿ the bird＿ was sing-ing, was sing - ing

Songs that will＿ nev - er grow old. ＿＿

The sign ⌢ over the first note in the fifth phrase means
that you should hold the note a little longer when you sing
it. This sign is called a "hold" or a "fermata" (fĕr-mä′ tä).
Find another fermata in the song.

RHYTHM

Every song has rhythm. Notes make the rhythm of a song. They tell us when to sing fast and when to sing slowly.

Here are the kinds of notes you use when you sing many of your songs. Clap and say each note with "tah." When you see a rest, clap but do not say anything.

Quarter Notes

Quarter Notes and Rests

Eighth Notes

Eighth Notes and Rests

Half Notes

Half Note and Rest

The Postman

Adapted   Music by Josephine Wolverton

STEADILY

1. The whis-tling post-man swings a-long,
2. The post-man's walk-ing   up   our street,

His   bag   is   deep and   wide;
Soon   now he'll   ring   my   bell;

And mes-sag - es   from   all   the world
Per-haps there'll be   a   let - ter stamped

Are   bun - dled   up   in - side.
In   A - sia, who   can   tell?

You sing many quarter notes in "The Postman." Now sing it in another way. Instead of quarter notes, sing half notes (♩ ♩). How would the postman walk to this rhythm?

Sing the song with eighth notes (♫).

23

Song of the Week

BRIGHTLY

Adapted Words   American Folk Tune

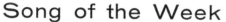

1. Mon-day morn-ing go to school; Mon-day eve-ning, home;

Get your ball and get your bat, And we'll go walk-ing home.

2. Tuesday morning go to school; Tuesday evening, home;
   There's a program on TV; Come on, let's hurry home.

3. Wednesday morning go to school; Wednesday evening, home;
   Come, let's play a game of tag As we go walking home.

4. Thursday morning go to school; Thursday evening, home;
   Come on over to my house As we go walking home.

5. Friday morning go to school; Friday evening, home;
   School is over for this week, Let's do just as we please.

24

Take a partner and step lightly to the rhythm of the song:

> 1 2 3 | > 1 2 3 |

Come, Dance

IN WALTZ TIME

Creole Folk Song

Come, dance with me! Don't step on my toes!

And if you fall, don't fall on your nose!

Let's join both our hands and then turn a - bout,

(spoken)

We'll cir-cle a-round and end with a shout. Hey!

Rhythm Everywhere

Words and Music by Richard C. Berg

FAST, BRIGHTLY

1. There's rhy - thm in the heart - beat,
2. There's rhy - thm in a mo - tor,

There's rhy-thm in a band that march-es down the street,
There's rhy-thm in a wheel that rolls a - long the street,

Refrain
There's rhy-thm, rhy-thm ev-'ry-where That makes me tap my feet.

Whistle

You'll find it makes no dif-f'rence where you are,

There is rhy - thm, rhy-thm ev - 'ry - where.

26

Happy Birthday

Words by Lou Ann Hatcher
Music by Robert Pace

BRIGHTLY

A hap - py birth-day we wish for you,

We'll sing you a birth - day song; ___

We wish you joy ___ and pleas-ure to - day

And the whole year long. _____

27

How many quarter rests do you see?

The Little Red Boat

Words and Music by Daniel Hooley

ONE SWING TO A MEASURE

A fish-er-man once had a boat,_____

And the boat was paint-ed red;_____

And ev-'ry day as he sailed a-way,

The fish-er-man soft-ly said:_____

softly

"What a ver-y nice boat to sail the sea!

What a ver-y nice boat, it just suits me!

I'm the hap-pi-est salt-wa-ter fish-er-man

On the sea, the deep blue sea."

29

Jungle Drums

Words and Music by Stephen Scott

WITH A STEADY BEAT

Bin-gle bun-gle in the jun-gle, When they want to tel-e-phone,

Bin-gle bun-gle in the jun-gle, Drums beat out a deep, low tone;

Boom boom boom boom boom! "How are you to - day?"

Boom - a - boom boom boom boom! Jun-gle drums talk that way.

Drums play

Gong plays

Rattles or sticks play

30

Make up messages. Play each one several times. Then someone can play an answer. Here is an example:

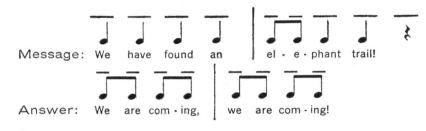

Message: We have found an el-e-phant trail!

Answer: We are com-ing, we are com-ing!

🔊 Music Making   Paraphrase   Panamanian Folk Song

STEADILY   G   G   G

1. I can make my drum go boom boom!
2. If the day is gray and drear-y,

G   D7

Hear the mer-ry sound of beat-ing,
And you need a lit-tle pleas-ure,

D7   D7

Ma - ra - cas, sticks, and bon-gos,
You'll bright-en up the school-room

D7   G

Ev - 'ry - one the tune re-peat-ing.
With the beat-ing of the meas-ure.

INDIANS

Indians lived in our country long before the white men came here. Some tribes lived in the woods country, while others lived on the plains, in the hills and mountains, and along the seashores.

The tribes who lived in villages had small farms. They raised corn of many colors: white, yellow, blue, purple, and red. All of these tribes had some customs that were the same. They prayed to their Sun God to make the corn grow and to give them light and warmth. They also prayed to him for rain for the growing corn.

The songs that follow in this book are from Indian tribes in our country. They are in English, so that you can sing them. Each tribe, however, spoke its own language and sang songs in that language.

The Indians sang and danced while some of them played drums and rattles.

Song to the Sun

Zuni Song

Wake! A-wake! A-wake! Wake! A-wake! A-wake!

The sun has come and the moon has gone,

We greet the sun with our morn-ing song,

We are thank-ful for an - oth-er day,

We are thank-ful for an - oth-er day.

Wake! A-wake! A-wake! Wake! A-wake! A-wake!

Many Indian tribes sang a hymn to the sun every morning. They raised their arms and lowered them to the rhythm of the words.

Play the song on your rhythm instruments.

Drum beat

Shakers and Gourds

Work Song

Dakota Indian Song

1. To our work we must go,
2. To our work we must go,

To the fields and to the riv - er,
To the for - est and the moun - tain,

To our work we go, To our work we go.
To our work we go, To our work we go.

In the morning, the Indian men went to their work.
Some of them went to catch fish for the family.
Others took their bows and arrows into the woods
and the mountains to hunt animals for food.

In some tribes, the squaws used to wear bird feathers on each wrist while they ground corn to make into little cakes. They sang while they ground the corn. The men of the tribe danced as the women sang.

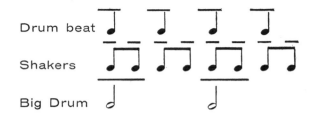

Drum beat

Shakers

Big Drum

Corn - Grinding Song

Navajo Song

The squaws are grind-ing corn on flat rocks. Hey ya hey ya ho!

They grind the red corn on the flat rocks. Hey ya hey ya ho!

The white corn and yel-low corn they're grind-ing. Hey ya ho!

With pray'r feath-ers on their wrists they're grind-ing. Hey ya ho!

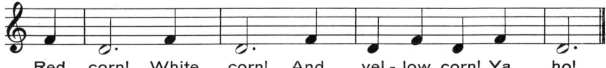

Red corn! White corn! And yel-low corn! Ya ho!

35

Prayer for Rain

Based on an Indian Chant

The great Sun Fa-ther sends the rain,

The great Sun Fa-ther sends the snow.

Send us rain! Send us rain!

Send us rain up - on the plain

And make the storm winds blow!

Send us rain! Send us rain!

Indians used rattles to make the sound of rain.
They used drums to make the sound of thunder.

36

Play the drum very softly or use bells when you sing.

Lullaby

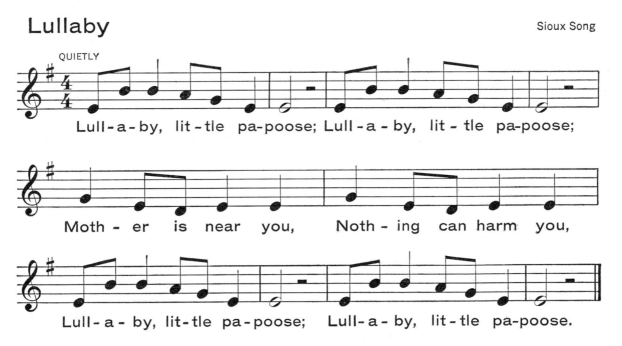

QUIETLY

Lull-a-by, lit-tle pa-poose; Lull-a-by, lit-tle pa-poose;

Moth - er is near you, Noth - ing can harm you,

Lull-a-by, lit-tle pa-poose; Lull-a-by, lit-tle pa-poose.

Most of the time, the Indian women stayed at home to
weed the corn, cook, sew, and look after the small chil-
dren. Indians were very kind and good to their children.

Sunset

Based on an Indian Tune

SMOOTHLY

Now the moon_ is in the sky, To the sun_ we say good-by;

Fa-ther Sun sleeps in the West, In the sky_ we see the moon;

gradually softer to the end

Shad-ows creep,_the night comes soon; Fa-ther Sun sleeps in the West,

And his peo-ple go to_ rest.

◐ Gold and Silver

Words by Joan Hurst   German Folk Tune

NOT TOO SLOWLY

Gold and sil - ver I a-dore, I can al-ways use it;

If I had a pock-et full, I would nev - er lose it;

Gold-en sun is my de-light, Sil-ver moon–beams thrill me;

Gold and sil - ver of the sky With a glad-ness fill me,

Gold and sil - ver of the sky With a glad-ness fill me.

As you sing the song, notice that some of the phrases have the same rhythm.

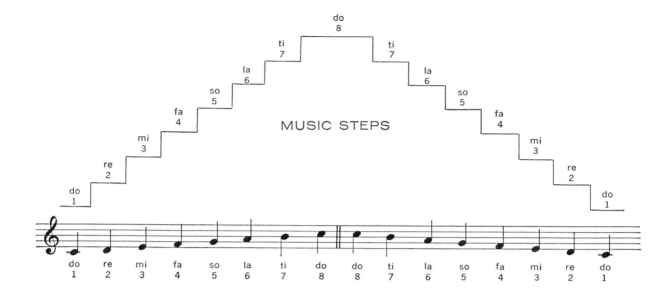

MUSIC STEPS

Melodies

Melodies sometimes rise a step,
Or on a single tone they stay;
They sometimes skip both high and low
—Tunes are made that way.

do re mi fa so la ti do
1　2　3　4　5　6　7　8

Taffy

Old Rhyme　Scale Song

OLD RHYME

Taf - fy was a Welsh - man, Taf - fy was a thief,

Taf - fy came to our house and stole a leg of beef;

I went to Taf - fy's house, Taf - fy was not home,

Taf - fy came to our house and stole a mar-row bone;

I went to Taf - fy's house, Taf - fy was in bed,

I took a mar-row bone and hit him on the head. (Whack!)

Sing the song and play the song on your melody instruments.

The melody starts high and then goes down low, like leaves falling from the trees in autumn. Chant the words in rhythm before singing and playing the song.

Autumn Leaves

Slovak Folk Tune

1. See the leaves   fall-ing down,
2. Soon the trees   will be bare

Leaves of red and   gold and brown;
In   the   win-ter's   chill - y   air;

Au - tumn leaves   twirl   a - round,
Au - tumn leaves   twirl   a - round,

Fall - ing   to   the   ground.
Fall - ing   to   the   ground.

do ti la so fa mi re do
8 7 6 5 4 3 2 1

Chant the words in rhythm before you sing.

The Elevator

Words and Music by Mary Massey

1. Up to the eighth floor, Up to the top,
2. Toys on the eighth floor, O - pen the door,

Down past the floors till it's time to stop.
Let's look a - round and then shop some more.

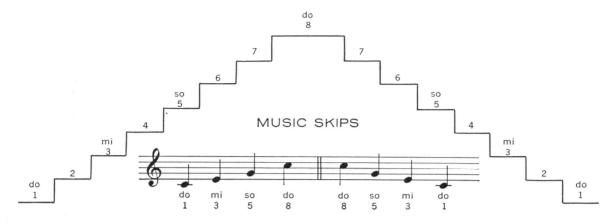

MUSIC SKIPS

The first phrase goes up stepwise.
The rest of the song skips downward to the last two measures.
The last two measures go down stepwise.

Row Your Boat

Traditional Song

Row, row, row your boat Gen-tly down the stream,—

Mer-ri-ly, mer-ri-ly, mer-ri-ly, mer-ri-ly, Life is but a dream.—

44

There are many skipwise tunes in this song. Can you find them?
What phrases are nearly alike?
Look at the melody as you hear it sung or played.

Down in the Meadow

Southern Folk Song

1. Down in the mead-ow, hop a doo-dle, hop a doo-dle,
2. Down in the barn-yard, hop a doo-dle, hop a doo-dle,

Down in the mead-ow, hop a doo-dle doo!
Down in the barn-yard, hop a doo-dle doo!

Down in the mead-ow the colt be-gan to prance,
Down in the barn-yard the goose be-gan to sing,

The cow be-gan to whis-tle, and the pig be-gan to dance.
The hen be-gan to cack-le as the roos-ter flapped a wing.

Jenny - O!

American Play Party Song

GAILY

1. Two in the cen-ter and you swing your Jen-ny,

Two in the cen-ter and you swing your Jen-ny,

Two in the cen-ter and you swing your Jen-ny,

Swing your Jen-ny - O!

2. Four in the center and you swing your Jenny,
(Sing 3 times.)
Swing your Jenny-O!

3. Eight hands around and we'll all swing Jenny,
(Sing 3 times.)
All swing Jenny-O!

4. Go to the barn and take a look at Jenny,
(Sing 3 times.)
Look at Jenny-O!

5. Now promenade while we all swing Jenny,
(Sing 3 times.)
All swing Jenny-O!

Play the tune on your melody instruments.

Stepwise / Skipwise

do ti la so so do so
8 7 6 5 5 8 5

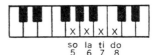

so la ti do
5 6 7 8

Up in the Steeple (4 - tone song)

Up in the stee-ple, sing to the peo-ple, Ding dong, ding ding dong!

Ring in the day-time, ring in the night-time, Ding dong, ding ding dong!

47

Laughing Town

Adapted Words   German Folk Tune

WELL ACCENTED

Oh, there is a place where they laugh all the day,

Hi did - dle dee did - dle doh;

When - ev - er a fun - ny thing hap - pens, they say:

You can play some of the phrases on your melody instruments.

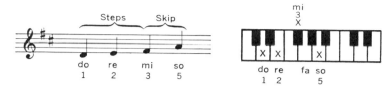

There are only four different tones in "The Merry-Go-Round."
Chant the words in rhythm, and then sing and play the song.

🎵 The Merry - Go - Round (4 - tone song)

1. Round and   a - round goes the   mer - ry - go - round;
2. Ten cents a   ride, and you   might get one   free;

Nev - er goes   an - y - where,   just turns a - round.
Just catch the   brass ring, now   try it and   see.

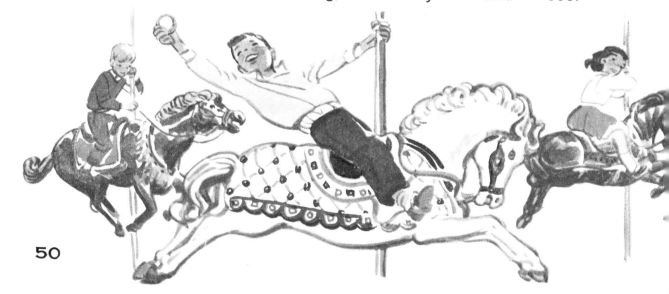

Steps

mi re do
3   2   1

What kinds of notes and rests do you see?

The Storm (3 - tone song)

1. Light-ning   flash!   Thun - der   crash!
2. Zing zing   roar!   See   it   pour!

Soon the clouds will o - pen, and the   rain will   splash.
Storm-y winds are push-ing at   our kitch-en   door.

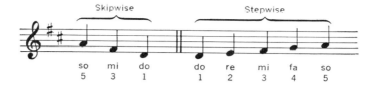

Skipwise — Stepwise

so mi do | do re mi fa so
5 3 1 | 1 2 3 4 5

Circus Performers (5 - tone song)

1. Cir-cus per-form-ers with won-der-ful ease

Swing back and forth on the fly-ing tra-peze.

2. Some walk on wires that swing in the air,
   Balancing lightly, it seems without care.

3. Circus performers must time ev'ry feat,
   That's why the band plays a rhythmical beat.

○ Soap Bubbles

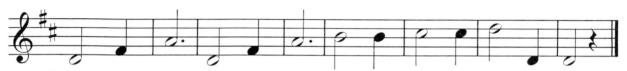

1. Fill the pipe! Gen-tly blow! Now you'll see the bub-bles grow.
2. Fill the pipe! Gen-tly blow! In the sun-light see them glow.

Strong at first, then they burst, And they go to noth-ing, Oh!
Pink and blue, green-ish too, They go drift-ing high and low.

What phrases have the same rhythm?

Lucy Locket

Lu-cy Lock-et lost her pock-et, What a sil-ly thing to do!

If you are not care-ful, Lu-cy, Next you'll lose your shoe.

The note without a stem is called a "whole note." We hold it for four beats:

In this song it is tied to a quarter note, and so we hold the two notes for five beats:

Every Night

Mountain Folk Song

SMOOTHLY, NOT TOO SLOWLY

1. Ev - 'ry night___ when the sun goes in,___

Ev - 'ry night___ when the sun goes in,___

Ev - 'ry night___ when the sun goes in,

I hang down my head __ and, mourn-ful, cry. __

2.
If the stars in the sky won't shine,
If the stars in the sky won't shine,
If the stars in the sky won't shine,
I hang down my head and, mournful, cry.

3.
If the moon hides behind a cloud,
If the moon hides behind a cloud,
If the moon hides behind a cloud,
I hang down my head and, mournful, cry.

The Harmonica

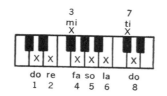

Korean Folk Song

IN A SPRIGHTLY MANNER

John-ny's un - cle gave to him a new har-mon - i - ca;

Self-ish John - ny would not share it, said: "It's just for me!"

Then he went a - way to vis - it, leav-ing it at home.

Lit-tle broth-er pounced up - on it; "Now I'll play," said he.

Do re mi fa so la ti do! "Oh, what fun to try!"
(1 2 3 4 5 6 7 8)

Do mi so do, do so mi do! "A mu - si - cian, I!"
(1 3 5 8, 8 5 3 1)

55

Play the first note in each measure on your melody instruments.

The End of Day (5 - tone song)

Words by Sir Henry Newbolt

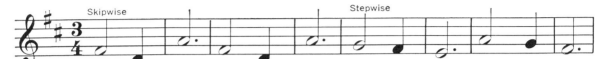

Night is come, Owls are out; Bee-tles hum Round a-bout;

Chil-dren snore Safe in bed; Noth-ing more Need be said.

Stars

I'm glad the stars are over me
And not beneath my feet,
Where we would trample on them
Like cobbles on the street;
I think it is a happy thing
That they are set so far;
It's best to have to look up high
When you would see a star.

Make up a tune for the poem.

56

There are two kinds of notes in "The Sky." What are they?
How many quarter rests do you see?

The Sky

Words and Music by Robert Pace

1. As you sit and watch the sky,
2. When the sun is in the sky,

Do you won-der how and why
Though the stars still shine on high,

Stars all twin-kle through the night,
You can't see their twin-kling light,

When it's morn-ing fade from sight?
Sun-shine dims them from your sight.

57

Chant the words in rhythm before you sing the song.

The Race

Skipwise · Stepwise · Skipwise

1. One said to the oth-er, Go-ing to the store:

Stepwise

"I'll buy you a can-dy bar And race you to the door!"

2. Off they went together, Down the street they tore,
Each fell down and bumped his head While racing to the door.

3. Each said to the other, Just inside the door,
"What did we come here to buy? I can't remember now."

Dinosaur Diet

Adapted Words   Slovak Folk Tune

Long a - go a * di - no - saur__ lived in our own state,

He had a health - y ap - pe - tite, and this is what he   ate:

Green leaves and   tops of trees,   small plants and   tall weeds;

What a fun - ny   di - et! I would-n't like to   try it.

* bron-to-saur-us

59

Sweet Kitty Clover

Adapted from an English Folk Song

WITH QUICK MOTION

1. Sweet Kit - ty Clo - ver is rath - er slow,
2. Nice Bil - ly Do - ver, he both-ers me so,

1, 2. Oh, oh, oh, oh! Oh, oh, oh, oh!

Sweet Kit - ty Clo - ver is rath - er slow,
Nice Bil - ly Do - ver, he both-ers me so,

End

1, 2. Oh, oh, oh, oh, oh, oh!_____

60

She's three feet tall, and that I prize
His face is round and red and fat

Go to the beginning.

As just a fit wife for a man of my size.
Like hol - ly ber-ries, or red-der than that.

What phrases look and sound alike?

The Wind Song

Words by Cecil Cowdrey   Russian Folk Tune

FAST

1. When the snow is fly - ing, Hear the North Wind cry-ing!

loudly   *softly*

Ooh___ Hear it blow! Ooh___ See it snow!

2. When the raindrops patter, listen how they chatter!
   Ooh, how they splash on my window sash!

3. When the bees are humming, then vacation's coming!
   Ooh, but it's near! Ooh, almost here!

61

As you listen to the song sung or played for the first time, find the phrases that are stepwise and the phrases that are skipwise.

Poor Old Man

American Folk Song

CRISPLY

1. Oh, a poor old_ man came_ rid - ing_ by,

Says I, "Old man, your horse will die!"

Oh, John-ny, come to Hi-lo; Oh, poor old man!

Refrain   F   F

Oh,   wake   her!   Oh,   shake   her!

F   F   D min.   C7

Oh,   shake that   girl   with   the   red   dress   on,

F   Bb   F   C7   F

Oh, John-ny, come to   Hi - lo;   Oh, poor old man!

2. Oh, the poor old man just looked at me
   And hitched his horse up to a tree,
   Oh, Johnny, come to Hilo; Oh, poor old man!

3. Oh, the poor old man, he scratched his head;
   And while he scratched, his horse dropped dead.
   Oh, Johnny, come to Hilo; Oh, poor old man!

4. Oh, the poor old man, his name was John.
   This song's so sad, I can't go on.
   Oh, Johnny, come to Hilo; Oh, poor old man!

Sailors on the old sailing ships used to sing this chantey as they worked in rhythm to the tune.

Here is the rhythm for the second and fourth phrases and some things that you can do while you are singing them:

jump
clap
drum

jump
clap
drum

clap - - - - - - - - - - - - - -
turn around
use shakers

Moon's a - Rising

American Folk Song

WELL ACCENTED

1. Moon's a - ris-ing on Thun-der-head Moun-tain,

Hey! Hey! Step and go ____ light - ly!

Hound dogs bay-ing and we'll go a - hunt-ing,

Hey! Hey! Step and go ____ light - ly,

2. Chased a 'coon into a gum tree,
Hey! Hey! Step and go lightly!
Shot the 'coon and hit a froggie
Hey! Hey! Step and go lightly!

3 Had a possum up in a tree there
Hey! Hey! Step and go lightly!
Shook that tree and down came a he-bear,
Hey! Hey! Step and go lightly!

64

4. Mister Bear, please don't catch me, sir,
   Hey! Hey! Step and go lightly!
   Catch that fellow behind that tree, sir,
   Hey! Hey! Step and go lightly!

5. Moon's going down, my song is ended,
   Hey! Hey! Step and go lightly!
   Mighty good thing, for I'm pretty nigh winded,
   Hey! Hey! Step and go lightly!

Halloween Scare

Words by Julie Gibault   Music by Daniel Hooley

MYSTERIOUSLY

1. Scare me with witch-es in tall black hats,
2. Grin, Jack-o'-lan-tern, and make me shake,

Scare me with gob-lins and scare me with bats.
Creak, rust-y hing-es, I'm wait-ing to quake.

Refrain

See how I shiv-er? Boo-hoo! Boo-hoo!

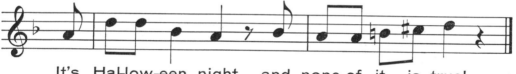

It's Hallow-een night, and none of it is true!

65

The sign ‖: :‖ means "repeat."

Lucy Long

IN A LIVELY MANNER

Adapted Words   Old American Song

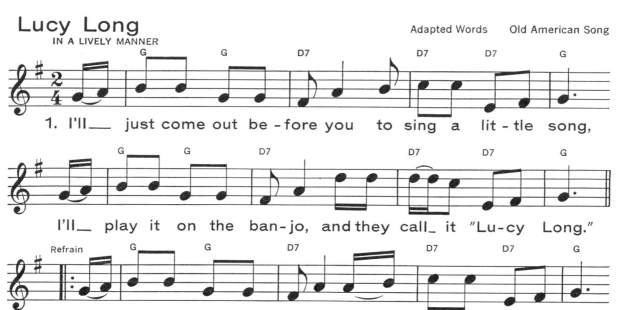

1. I'll__ just come out be - fore you to sing a lit - tle song,

I'll__ play it on the ban - jo, and they call__ it "Lu-cy Long."

Refrain

Oh,__ take your time, Miss Lu-cy, take your time, Miss Lu-cy Long,
Now__ all join hands and cir-cle and __ step a-round the hall,

Oh,__ take your time, Miss Lu - cy, take your time, Miss Lu-cy Long,
Then__ go back where you came from; sa - lute now, one and all.

2. Miss Lucy, she is handsome; Miss Lucy, she is tall;
   Whenever she comes walking, She's the prettiest of them all.

Make up your own way to play this game.
"Salute" means "bow to your partner."

Walk Along, John

Southern Folk Game

1. Come on, boys, and hush your talk - ing,
2. Come on, girls, and stop your pok - ing,

Walk a - long, John, walk a - long;
Walk a - long, John, walk a - long;

All join in and let's go walk - ing,
Hur - ry home, the stove is smok - ing,

Walk a - long, John, walk a - long.
Walk a - long, John, walk a - long.

You can also "hop along," "skip along," and "run along."

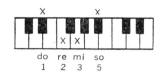 

The Tower (4 - tone song)

French Folk Song

All: **1.** The tow'r stands read-y, the tow'r stands read-y,

For war, read - y for war.____

2. TOWER:
I am not ready, I am not ready for war, ready for war.

3. CAPTAIN:
I'll ask King Louis, I'll ask King Louis to come, come to our aid.

4. TOWER:
Go ask King Louis, go ask King Louis to come, come to our aid.

5. CAPTAIN:
Please come, King Louis, please come, King Louis, please come, come to our aid.

6. KING:
I'm very busy, I'm very busy, please come another day.

7. CAPTAIN:
We need some soldiers, we need some soldiers to wage, wage war today.

8. KING:
I'll send enforcements, I'll send enforcements to wage, wage war today.

9. ALL:
Our King and Sovereign, our King and Sovereign, please lead, lead them today.

10. KING:
I'll lead your armies, I'll lead your armies, I'll lead, lead them today.

11, ALL:
Here comes King Louis, here comes King Louis, he's come, come to our aid.

68

do ti la so fa mi re do
8 7 6 5 4 3 2 1

Building a House

Adapted Words   Slovak Folk Song

Group 1 plays or claps   Group 2 plays or claps

1. Tap a tap, tap a tap, Ham-mer on the wall,—

Group 1   Group 2

Tap a tap, tap a tap, Build the house up tall.—

2. Carpenter, carpenter, Make the sawdust fly,
   Saw the wood, trim the wood, Build the house up high.

3. Slap a slap, slap a slap, Paint from morn till night,
   Slap a slap, slap a slap, Paint it green and white.

do re mi fa so la
1 2 3 4 5 6

My Dog Bran (6 - tone song)

1. "Have you seen my dog Bran, Cock-er span-iel with a coat of tan?

2. "Just today he ran out, He's too small to find his way about."
3. "Come here, Bill, I see Bran, He is hiding near the old trash can."

so fa mi re do
5 4 3 2 1

Some Folks Do (5 - tone song)   Adapted Words   Music by Stephen Foster

1. Some folks like to sigh, Some folks do, some folks do,
2. Some folks fret and scold, Some folks do, some folks do,

Some folks like to cry, That's not for me or you.
Oth-ers' hearts are cold, That's not for me or you.

70

so mi fa re la fa
5 3 4 2 6 4

Night Time

Spanish Folk Song

Skipwise

Gay lit - tle hap - py moon-beams
Shine in the twin-kling star - light.

Dance thro' my o - pen win - dow,
I call them night-time's rain - bow.

The Horn

Adapted Words   German Folk Tune

QUIETLY

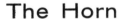

1. I can hear a horn sound-ing far off on the hill - side,
2. You can hear it too, if you lis-ten in the twi - light,

Ta ra ra! Sound - ing on the hill.
Ta ra ra! When the air is still.

mi mi mi so mi fa mi la la so mi fa so mi

A few of you may play this melody while the class sings "The Lamplighter."

The Lamplighter (6-tone song)

Paraphrase   Spanish Folk Song

SLOWLY

1. Pe-dro, the lamp-light-er, comes a-round each night,
2. As he walks, he sings a song and rings a bell,

Climbs his lad-der, cleans the lamp, and makes a light.
"Lamps are light-ed, my good peo-ple, all is well!"

72

so mi do | do ti la so fa mi re do
5 3 1 | 8 7 6 5 4 3 2 1

November Twilight

Adapted Words   Czech Folk Tune

Frost's in the air now, All the trees are bare now,

Gray shad-ows creep, Cold breez-es blow;

Day-light is dy-ing, With-ered leaves are fly-ing,

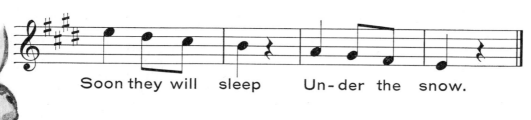

Soon they will sleep Un-der the snow.

73

Over the River and Through the Wood

BRIGHTLY

Words by Lydia Maria Child   Traditional Song

1. O - ver the riv - er   and through the wood,
2. O - ver the riv - er   and through the wood

To grand - fa - ther's house we   go;___
And straight through the barn - yard gate,___

The horse knows the way   to car-ry the sleigh
We seem ___   to   go   ex-treme - ly slow,

Through the white and drift - ed snow; —
It — is so hard to wait! —

O - ver the riv - er and through the wood,
O - ver the riv - er and through the wood

Oh, how — the wind does blow! —
Now grand-moth-er's cap I spy! —

It stings — the toes and — bites the nose
Hur - rah for the fun! Is the pud-ding done?

As o - ver the ground we go. —
Hur - rah for the pump - kin pie! —

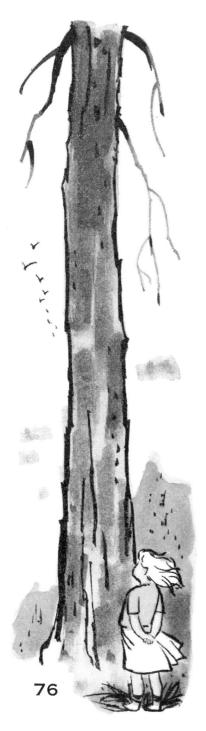

Gifts of God

Old American Song

1. For this new morn-ing with its light,
2. For blue of stream and blue of sky,

For rest and shel-ter of the night,
For pleas-ant shade of branch-es high,

For health and food, for love and friends,
For fra-grant air and cool-ing breeze,

For ev-'ry-thing His good-ness sends,
For beau-ty of the bloom-ing trees,

For all these gifts we thank Him.
For all these gifts we thank Him.

My Canary

Paraphrase   Spanish Folk Song

SMOOTHLY AND NOT TOO FAST

1. My ca-nar-y flew a-way, Left his cage the oth-er day;
2. If you see my yel-low bird, Won't you tell him that you heard

How I miss his lit-tle tune! Oh, I wish he'd come back soon.
Of a child who looks each day For his bird that flew a-way?

My lit-tle bird, my lit-tle bird,

Please list-en to my wish and come back soon!

The tunes in "My Canary" sound much alike, but each tune
is one note lower than the tune before it. In the Refrain,
each tune starts one note lower than the tune before it.

77

Where Are You Going, Shepherd? French Folk Song

1. "Where a - way, O shep-herd, where a - way?"

"To the man-ger cra-dle, where the ba - by lies."

2. "Is he fair, O shepherd, is he fair?"
‖: "Fairer than the moonbeams, fairer than the sun." :‖

3. "Who is there, O shepherd, who is there?"
‖: "Joseph, his good father, stands beside the crib." :‖

4. "And who else, O shepherd, and who else?"
‖: "Mary, the good mother, smiles upon her son." :‖

5. "No one else, O shepherd, no one else?"
"I see four small angels and I hear them sing
Praises to our Father, God the Heav'nly King."

A few of you may play this melody while the class sings the song.
Or you may play it as a bell solo while the class sings.

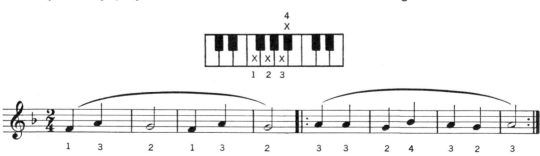

78

Child of God

NOT TOO FAST

1. If an-y-bod-y asks you who I am, —
2. The lit-tle cra-dle rocks to-night in glo - ry,
3. — Peace on earth, — Ma-ry, rock the cra - dle,

Who I am, —————— Who I am, —
Night in glo - ry, Night in glo - ry,
Rock the cra - dle, Rock the cra - dle,

If an - y - bod - y asks you who I am, —
The lit - tle cra-dle rocks to - night in glo - ry,
— Peace on earth, — Ma - ry, rock the cra - dle,

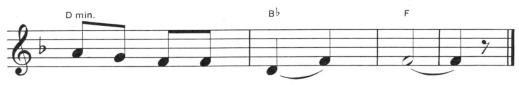

Tell him I'm a child of God. —
Rocks to-night in glo - ry. —
Ma - ry, rock the cra - dle. —

79

♦ Father Christmas

Carl Reinecke

GAILY

Bells, Triangle   Bells, Tri.

1,2,3. Ring cling - a   ring!

Bells, Tri.   Bells, Tri.

Cling - a - ling - a   bell, cling   ring!

1. Let me in, dear chil-dren, I - cy winds are blow-ing,

Won't you give me shel-ter? Here out-side it's snow-ing!

80

1,2,3. Ring cling-a ring!

Cling-a-ling-a bell, cling ring, cling-a ring!

2. Boys and girls, now listen! Open up your house door!
   I have toys and presents, ev'rything you long for.

3. Let the joy of Christmas fill your hearts and voices!
   Let me in, dear children, all the world rejoices.

Bells play

Seven Joys of Christmas

Adapted Words
American Folk Tune

TWO PULSES TO EACH MEASURE

1. The first— good joy that Christ-mas brings,
   To buy— and wrap the Christ-mas gifts

It is the joy— of one —
And hide them, ev - 'ry one.—

Refrain

We wish you joy at Christ-mas - tide—

And joy through-out the com - ing year;

May— all the world join in our song,

The song of Christ - mas cheer.—

2. The second good joy that Christmas brings,
   It is the joy of two
   To send out greeting cards by mail
   To friends both old and new.

3. The third good joy that Christmas brings,
   It is the joy of three
   To make and hang the ornaments
   Upon the Christmas tree.

4. The fourth good joy that Christmas brings,
   It is the joy of four
   To hang a wreath of holly green
   Upon the entry door.

5. The fifth good joy that Christmas brings,
   It is the joy of five
   To help prepare a Christmas feast
   Before the guests arrive.

6. The sixth good joy that Christmas brings,
   It is the joy of six
   To build a fire upon the hearth
   And light the candlesticks.

7. The seventh good joy that Christmas brings,
   It is the joy of seven
   To praise the Lord for all His gifts,
   They are the joys of Heav'n.

Deck the Hall

Old Welsh Carol

GAILY

1. Deck the hall with boughs of hol-ly, } Fa la la la la la la la la!
2. See the blaz-ing Yule be-fore us, }

'Tis the sea-son to be jol-ly, } Fa la la la la la la la la!
Strike the harp and join the cho-rus, }

Don we now our gay ap-par-el, } Fa_ la la_ la la la la!
Fol-low me in mer-ry meas-ure, }

Troll the an-cient Yule-tide car-ol, } Fa la la la la la la la la!
While I tell of Yule-tide treas-ure, }

You can sing the last phrase with either the high notes
or the low notes. If you like, half of you may sing the high
notes and half of you the low notes at the same time.

84

The Skaters' Waltz

Adapted Words   Music by Emil Waldteufel

1. Skat - ing a - long, ___ sing - ing a song, ___
2. Smooth-ly we glide ___ from side to side, ___

We swing a - long to a waltz-ing tune. ___
We swing a - long to a waltz-ing tune. ___

How many skipwise
tunes can you find?

Skips

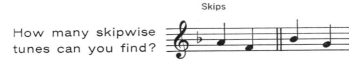

Lightning Bug (5 - tone song)

Words and Music by Robert Pace

1. Light - ning bug, light-ning bug, Shine your ti - ny light;
2. Light - ning bug, light-ning bug, Glow-ing in the dark,

Light - ning bug, light-ning bug, Twin-kling in the night!
Light - ning bug, light-ning bug, Light-ing up the park!

85

What kind of notes and rests do you find?
Play the song on your melody instruments.

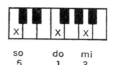

so   do   mi
5   1   3

so   do   mi
5   1   3

● The Shoemaker (3 - tone song)

Puerto Rican Song

1. "Oh,   my   chil-dren, where   will   you   go   to - day?"

"Oh,   shoe - mak - er,   we're   go - ing   out   to   play."

2. "My fine ladies, your shoes are old and worn."
   "O shoemaker, you'll fix them when they're torn."

3. "My fine ladies, I'll make them look like new."
   "O shoemaker, we give our thanks to you."

86

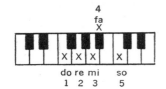

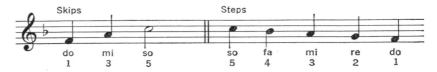

4
fa
X

do re mi   so
1 2 3   5

Skips   Steps

do   mi   so   so   fa   mi   re   do
1   3   5   5   4   3   2   1

Why Cats Wash After Eating (5-tone song)   Aesop   French Tune

Skipwise
F

1. Old cat caught a   fright-ened mouse, Ti - ri - li - ra, li - ra,

F

C7

F

In a tum - bled - down old house,   Ti - ri - li - ra - la.

MOUSE

2. "Were I you and in your place, Tirilira, lira,
   First, I'd wash my dirty face, Tirilirala."

CAT

3. "I will wash and be polite, Tirilira, lira,
   Then I'll eat you in one bite, Tirilirala."

4. Now the cat forgot his prey, Tirilira, lira,
   As he washed, mouse ran away, Tirilirala.

5. Ever since, a cat will eat, Tirilira, lira,
   Then he'll wash his face and feet, Tirilirala.

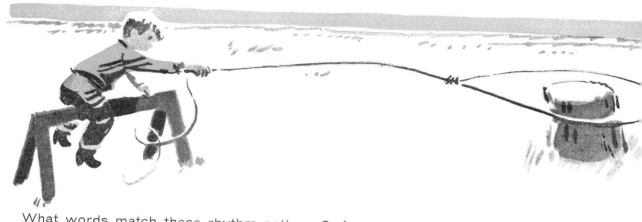

What words match these rhythm patterns? 1.___ ___ ___ ___ ___ ___ 2.___ ___ ___ ___ ___ ⸢

🔊 Tommy (5-tone song)

Adapted Words   English Folk Tune

1. Tom-my was a cow-boy, Tom-my was a cow-boy,

Tom-my was a cow-boy, And he could ride a horse.

Make a lit-tle mo-tion, Make a lit-tle mo-tion,

Make a lit-tle mo-tion, And be a cow-boy too.

2. Tommy was a cobbler, Tommy was a cobbler,
   Tommy was a cobbler, and he could mend a shoe.
   Make a little motion, make a little motion,
   Make a little motion, and be a cobbler too.

3. Tommy was a farmer, Tommy was a farmer,
   Tommy was a farmer, and he could plow the land.
   Make a little motion, make a little motion,
   Make a little motion, and be a farmer too.

4. Tommy drove a taxi, Tommy drove a taxi,
   Tommy drove a taxi, he watched the traffic signs.
   Make a little motion, make a little motion,
   Make a little motion, and drive a taxi too.

ti	do	re	mi	fa	so	la
7	1	2	3	4	5	6

Seasons (7 - tone song)

Words and Music by Richard C. Berg

1. Sum-mer brings the sun-shine, Win-ter brings the snow,
2. I like all the sea-sons. Which do you like best?

Fall brings au-tumn bon-fires, Spring makes flow-ers grow.
* _____ is the sea-son That I like the best.

*Name the one you like best: Springtime, Summer, Autumn, or Winter.

89

RHYTHM ACTIVITIES

On each measure, do something different.
Try making up some rhythms of your own, too.

2/4 step   knock

clap   step

3/4 walk   clap   sing "la"   jump

swing   swing   rest   step

4/4 step   clap   run in place   sway
drum   play triangle   play sticks   play piano or gong

Little Eskimo

Words by Bertha Freeman   Music by Daniel Hooley

MODERATELY

1. "Why is your house made of ice and snow,

Es - ki - mo, lit - tle Es - ki - mo?"

"My house is built where the cold winds blow,

All I have is ice and snow."

What phrases have the same rhythm pattern?

2. "Why is your suit made of fur and skin,
Eskimo, little Eskimo?"
"My suit is made of fur and skin
So the cold wind can't creep in."

3. "Just how long is your winter night,
Eskimo, little Eskimo?"
"For two whole months there is no light
On our longest winter night."

4. "What do you do on your long summer day,
Eskimo, little Eskimo?"
"That is the time when I play and play,
On our two-months summer day."

91

What phrases are alike?

When Shall We Be Married, John? (7 - tone song)

English Folk Song

She: 1. When shall we be mar-ried, John, mar-ried, John, mar-ried, John?
2. What shall I be mar-ried in, mar-ried in, mar-ried in?

When shall we be mar-ried, John, John, my lit - tle man?
What shall I be mar-ried in, John, my lit - tle man?

He: Sun-day morn-ing, to be sure, to be sure, to be sure,
A - pron and a cot-ton dress, cot-ton dress, cot-ton dress,

Sun-day morn-ing, to be sure. Why, the girl is mad!
A - pron and a cot-ton dress. Why, the girl is mad!

3. She: Can't I wear a finer dress, finer dress, finer dress?
Can't I wear a finer dress, John, my little man?
He: What are silks and satins for, satins for, satins for?
What are silks and satins for? Why, the girl is mad!

92

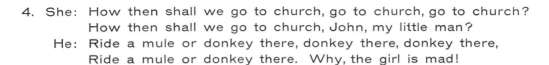

4. She: How then shall we go to church, go to church, go to church?
   How then shall we go to church, John, my little man?
   He: Ride a mule or donkey there, donkey there, donkey there,
   Ride a mule or donkey there. Why, the girl is mad!

5. She: Let's have something better, John, better, John, better, John,
   Let's have something better, John, John, my little man.
   He: What's a horse and carriage for, carriage for, carriage for,
   What's a horse and carriage for? Why, the girl is mad!

What phrases are alike?

Snow in the Night

Adapted Words   Music by Robert Franz

MODERATELY FAST AND SMOOTHLY

1. Yes - ter - day the moun - tain - side was green,
2. Now, to - day, a mag - ic land ap - pears,

Yes - ter - day the sky was fair and blue,——
Trees and bush-es clothed in robes of white,——

Then a mil - lion snow-flakes in the night
Hous - es trimmed with rows of i - cy lace!

Came fall - ing gen - tly to paint the world_ with_ white._
How beau - ti - ful this_ won-der-land_ of _ white!_

The Miller

Paraphrase   French Folk Song

1. "Why do you sleep when your mill goes too live - ly?
2. "Of course I sleep when my mill wheel goes live - ly,

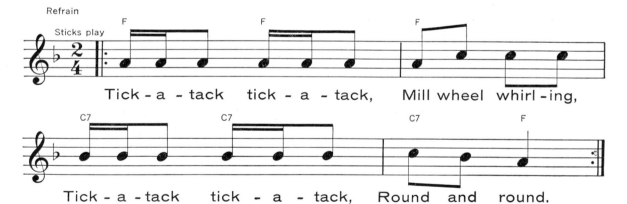

Why do you sleep when your mill goes too strong?"
Of course I sleep when my mill wheel goes strong!"

Refrain

Sticks play

Tick - a - tack   tick - a - tack,   Mill wheel whirl - ing,

Tick - a - tack   tick - a - tack,   Round and round.

With maracas and tambourines, play the rhythm of
the first measure throughout the song:

Taking a Trip (5 - tone song)

Folk Style

1.   If we should take a trip some day,
2. Let's go by bus to Mex - i - co,

We'll go   by   boat   or   plane,
Let's take   a   boat   to   Spain,

We'll go   by bus   or   we'll go   by   car,
We'll ride   a   car   to   Bo - liv - i - a,

We'll go   by   rail - road   train.
Then we'll come home   by   plane.

This song has the same rhythm pattern as "Taking a Trip."
Play the rhythm of the first measure throughout the song.

Mister Banjo (7 - tone song)

Creole Folk Song

1. Look at the dan-dy, see Mis-ter Ban-jo,

Car-ry-ing a bam-boo cane, Mis-ter Ban-jo,

Big cane that goes tap - tap, Mis - ter Ban-jo,

Big cane that goes tap - tap!

2. Look at the dandy, see Mister Banjo,
   He is wearing new boots, Mister Banjo,
   New boots that go squeak, squeak, Mister Banjo,
   New boots that go squeak, squeak!

3. Look at the dandy, see Mister Banjo,
   Looking at his fine gold watch, Mister Banjo,
   Gold watch that goes tick, tick, Mister Banjo,
   Gold watch that goes tick, tick!

GROUP 1:
On the first two phrases, clap or play this rhythm:

GROUP 2:
On phrases three and four, clap or play this rhythm:

Dad and I

Paraphrase   Polish Folk Song

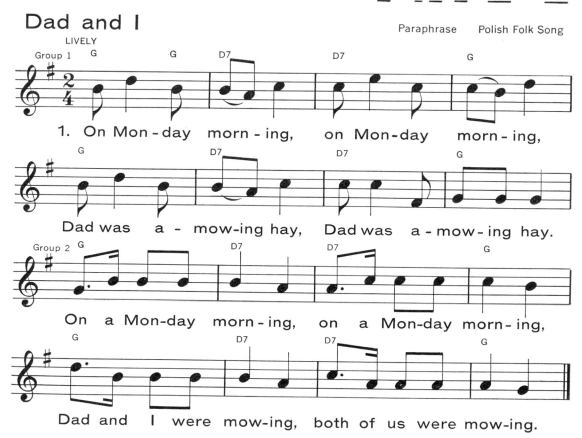

LIVELY

1. On Mon - day morn - ing, on Mon - day morn - ing,

Dad was a - mow-ing hay, Dad was a - mow - ing hay.

On a Mon-day morn - ing, on a Mon-day morn - ing,

Dad and I were mow-ing, both of us were mow-ing.

2. On Tuesday morning, on Tuesday morning,
Dad was a-raking hay, Dad was a-raking hay.
On a Tuesday morning, on a Tuesday morning,
Dad and I were raking, both of us were raking.

3. On Wednesday morning, etc.,
   Dad was a-drying hay, etc.

4. On Thursday morning, etc.,
   Dad was a-hauling hay, etc.

5. On Friday morning, etc.,
   Dad was a-selling hay, etc.

6. On Saturday morning, etc.,
   Dad was a-marketing, etc.

7. On Sunday morning, on Sunday morning,
   Dad took us all to church, Dad took us all to church.
   On a Sunday morning, on a Sunday morning,
   We all went to church then, we all went to church then.

○ Be My Valentine

Adapted Words   German Folk Tune

1. Will you   be, be, be, be, be, be, be my   Val - en - tine?
2. Yes, I'll   be, be, be, be, be, be, be your Val - en - tine!

1, 2. You know that   I'll   be yours   if on - ly you'll be mine.

1. Will you   be, be, be, be, be, be, be my   Val - en - tine?
2. Yes, I'll   be, be, be, be, be, be, be your   Val - en - tine!

1, 2. You know that I'll   be yours   if on - ly   you'll be mine.

You're a   faith - ful friend,   al - ways kind and   true;

It's no won-der I like to be with you.

1. Tell me that you, that you, that you'll be my Val-en-tine,
2. Yes, I'll be, I'll be, I'll be, I'll be your Val-en-tine,

Please, won't you prom-ise that you'll be my Val - en-tine?
Yes, I'll____ prom-ise that I'll be your Val - en-tine!

When You Send a Valentine

When you send a valentine,
That's the time for fun!
Push it underneath the door,
Ring the bell and run, run, run!
Ring the bell and run!

—Mildred Hill

Make up your own melody for this song.

Red Valentine

Words and Music by Mary Francis

1. I bought a pret-ty red val-en-tine
2. Here is a pret-ty red val-en-tine

Just for a ver-y spec-ial friend of mine,
Sent from a ver-y spec-ial friend of mine,

Rib-bons and lace and words so gay,
Rib-bons and lace and words which say:

I will mail it right a-way.
"Be my Val-en-tine to-day!"

Washington and Lincoln

Words and Music by Charles Crane

1. When Wash - ing - ton was ver - y young he liked the things I do, ___ He rode a po - ny, beat a drum, and ran some rac - es too. ___

2. When Lin - coln was a grow - ing boy he worked from dawn till night, ___ He bor-rowed books from all his friends and read by can - dle - light. ___

Refrain

Wash - ing - ton and Lin - coln helped make our coun - try great, ___ And when their birth-days come a-round we like to cel - e - brate. ___

America the Beautiful

Words by Katharine Lee Bates   Music by Samuel A. Ward

1. O beau-ti-ful for spa-cious skies, For am-ber waves of grain,
2. O beau-ti-ful for pil-grim feet Whose stern im-pas-sioned stress
3. O beau-ti-ful for pa-triot dream That sees be-yond the years

For pur-ple moun-tain maj-es-ties A-bove the fruit-ed plain!
A thor-ough-fare for free-dom beat A-cross the wil-der-ness!
Thine al-a-bas-ter cit-ies gleam Un-dimmed by hu-man tears!

A-mer-i-ca, A-mer-i-ca! God shed His grace on thee,
A-mer-i-ca, A-mer-i-ca! God mend thine ev-'ry flaw,
A-mer-i-ca, A-mer-i-ca! God shed His grace on thee,

And crown thy good with broth-er-hood From sea to shin-ing sea!
Con-firm thy soul in self-con-trol, Thy lib-er-ty in law!
And crown thy good with broth-er-hood From sea to shin-ing sea!

Throughout the song, beat on the drum:

Flag Song

Words by Eleanor Smith   Music by Nancy Kelly

IN MARCH TIME

1, 2. Sing for the flag, the Red, White, and Blue!

Flag of the free and flag of the true,

1. Flag of the no - ble, flag of the brave,
2. Long as the stars that shine up a - bove

O - ver the chil - dren proud - ly wave!
Shall it en - dure, the flag we love!

105

America

Words by Samuel Francis Smith   Music by Henry Carey

1. My coun - try,   'tis   of   thee, Sweet land   of
2. My na - tive   coun - try, thee, Land   of   the
3. Let mu - sic   swell the breeze, And ring from
4. Our fa - thers' God,   to Thee,   Au - thor of

lib - er - ty,   Of thee   I   sing;   Land where my
no - ble free, Thy name I   love;   I   love thy
all the trees Sweet free-dom's song; Let mor - tal
lib - er - ty,   To Thee we   sing;   Long may our

fa - thers died! Land of   the   Pil - grims' pride,
rocks and rills,   Thy woods and   tem - pled hills,
tongues a - wake, Let all that breathe par - take,
land   be bright   With free-dom's ho - ly   light;

From ev - 'ry_ moun-tain side, Let_ free-dom ring!
My heart_ with_ rap-ture thrills Like_ that a - bove.
Let rocks_their_ si - lence break, The_sound pro-long!
Pro - tect_ us _   by Thy might, Great_God, our King.

106

Play this as an Introduction to the song:

so do mi so
5 1 3 5

so do so do mi do mi so so so so
5 1 5 1 3 1 3 5 5 5 5

Brave Young Soldiers

Folk Song

Here come the brave young sol-diers
They're march-ing to the mu-sic

With their guns in hand, with their guns in hand;
Of a big brass band, of a big brass band.

They pass in close for - ma-tion, march-ing row on row;
They step in stead - y rhy-thm as they on-ward go.

When you come to the Slow Waltz, take a partner and join hands.
Step on tiptoe around the room:

Good Morning

Adapted Words   Danish Folk Game

Good morn-ing, good morn-ing, I'm glad to see you here.

Come, Ma - ry and Tom-my and Su - san and An - tho-ny,

Pe - ter and Nan - cy, Come, join in the dance.

The fid-dle now be - gins to play a waltz for us to dance.

Slow Waltz

G   D7   D7   G   G

(Sing la)

G   D7   D7   G

109

The Noble Duke of York

American Play Party Song

1. Oh, the no - ble__ Duke of__ York,
2. Now__ when they were up, they were up,

He had ten__ thou - sand__ men;
And when they were down, they were down;

He led them__ up to the top of the hill
And when they were on - ly__ half-way__ up,

And__ led them down a - gain.
They were nei - ther up nor down.

Who Will Shoe Your Foot

Appalachian Song

1. Oh, who will shoe your pret - ty foot,
2. My pa will shoe my pret - ty foot,

And who will glove your hand,
My ma will glove my hand,

And who will kiss your ru - by red lips
And none will kiss my ru - by red lips

When I've gone to a for - eign land?
Un - til John-ny comes home a - gain.

3. I'm sure you know the crow is black
   And sometimes purple-blue,
   If ever I prove false unto you
   May I melt like the morning dew.

4. Till all the seas run dry, my love,
   And rocks melt in the sun,
   I'll love you till the day that I die
   And then you'll know that I'm done.

111

Bingo

Adapted Words   Adapted American Folk Song

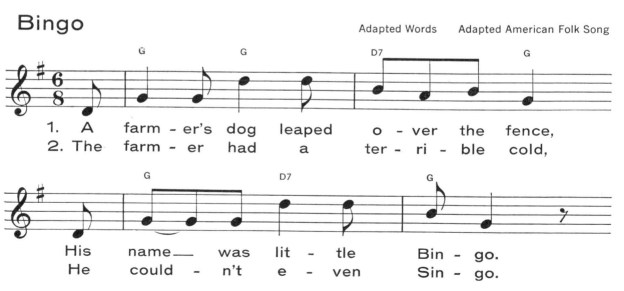

1. A farm - er's dog leaped o - ver the fence,
2. The farm - er had a ter - ri - ble cold,

His name__ was lit - tle Bin - go.
He could - n't e - ven Sin - go.

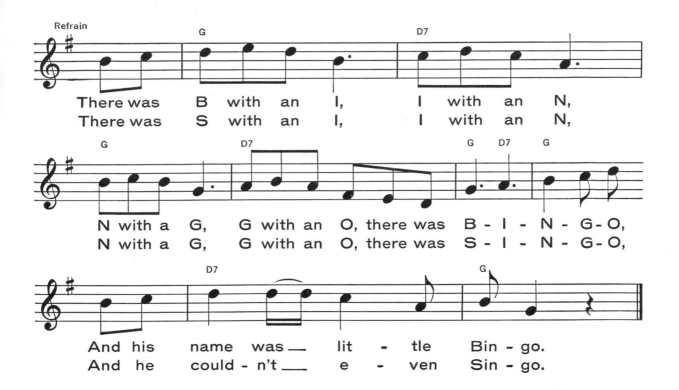

Refrain

There was B with an I, I with an N,
There was S with an I, I with an N,

N with a G, G with an O, there was B - I - N - G-O,
N with a G, G with an O, there was S - I - N - G-O,

And his name was — lit - tle Bin - go.
And he could - n't — e - ven Sin - go.

3. The farmer loved a pretty young maid,
   And gave her a wedding ringo.
   There was R with an I, I with an N,
   N with a G, G with an O, there was R-I-N-G-O,
   And he gave her a wedding ringo.

4. Now, don't you think this is a nice song?
   It surely is, by jingo.
   There's a J with an I, I with an N,
   N with a G, G with an O, there is J-I-N-G-O.
   Oh, it surely is, by jingo.

Around the Circle

Adapted Words   American Folk Game

1. First__ girl walks__ a - round the ring,
2. Swing__ your part-ner a - round in place,

A - round the ring, a - round the ring,
A - round in place, a - round in place,

First__ girl walks a - round the ring,
Prom - e - nade a - round the ring,

And then bows to her part - ner.
A - round the ring you go._____

3. Second girl walks around the ring, etc.
4. Swing your partner around in place, etc.

114

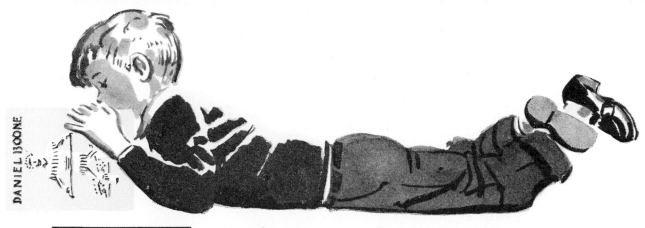

do re mi fa so la
1 2 3 4 5 6

do re mi fa so la
1 2 3 4 5 6

Daniel Boone (6 - tone song)

Words and Music by Josephine Wolverton

STEPWISE

1. I like books of men who lived long a - go,

Men who walked the trails and shot the buf - fa - lo.

2. Daniel Boone, a scout and a hunter bold,
   Traveled in the summer's heat and winter's cold..

3. When he saw the wealth of this great country,
   Told the folks to come out West where land was free.

4. Ev'rywhere he went, you would hear him say:
   "What a mighty nation this will be some day!"

115

As you sing, touch your head on the word "cap"; your throat on "scarf"; your ear on "olive oil"; and your heart on "lemon drops."

so   do   re   mi
5   1   2   3

My Burro (4 - tone song)

Spanish Folk Song

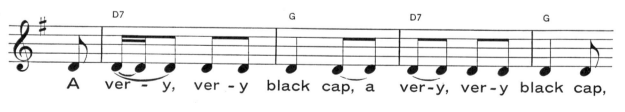

G   G   D7   G

1. Oh, my bur-ro, my bur-ro, his head is ach-ing bad-ly,

G   G   D7   G

The doc-tor put a black_ cap up - on his ach-ing head;

D7   G   D7   G

A ver - y, ver - y black cap, a ver-y, ver-y black cap,

D7   G   C   D7   G

Za - pa - ti -tos lee rah la   la,   Za - pa - ti -tos lee rah.

2. Oh, my burro, my burro, his throat is aching badly,
   The doctor put a white scarf upon his aching throat.
   A white scarf, a black cap, a white scarf, a black cap,
   Zapatitos lee rah la la, Zapatitos lee rah.

3. Oh, my burro, my burro, his ear is aching badly,
   The doctor gave him olive oil to cure his aching ear.
   O olive oil, a white scarf, a white scarf, a black cap,
   Zapatitos lee rah la la, Zapatitos lee rah.

4. Oh, my burro, my burro, his heart is aching badly,
   The doctor gave him lemon drops to cure his aching heart.
   O lemon drops, olive oil, a white scarf, a black cap,
   Zapatitos lee rah la la, Zapatitos lee rah.

117

do ti la so mi re do
1   7   6   5   3   2   1

Daughter, Will You Marry? Pennsylvania Dutch Folk Song

1. "Daugh-ter, will you mar-ry?" "Yea, Fa-ther, yea."

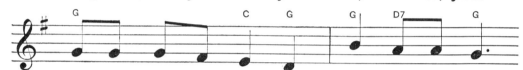

"Will you wed a farm-er?" "Nay, Fa-ther, nay.

A farm-er's wife I will not be,

Milk-ing_ cows is not for me, Nay, Fa-ther, nay."

2. "Daughter, will you marry?" "Yea, Father, yea."
   "Will you wed a doctor?" "Nay, Father, nay!
   A doctor's wife I will not be,
   Medicine is not for me. Nay, Father, nay!"

3. "Daughter, will you marry?" "Yea, Father, yea."
   "Will you wed a fiddler?" "Yea, Father, yea.
   A fiddler's wife I'll gladly be,
   Singing and dancing is for me. Yea, Father, yea!"

The Bells

Words and Music by Charles Fontaine

ONE SWING TO EACH MEASURE

1. Ring on our days of glad-ness, Gay bells, gay bells;
2. Clang in the hour of dan-ger, Loud bells, proud bells;

Ring on our days of glad-ness, Sweet and clear!___
Clang in the hour of dan-ger, Sound your call!___

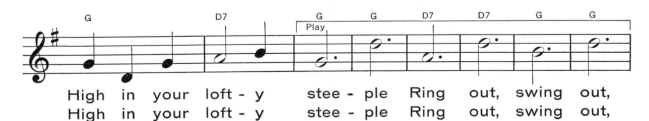

High in your loft-y stee-ple Ring out, swing out,
High in your loft-y stee-ple Ring out, swing out,

Call-ing the bus-y peo-ple, Far and near!___
Warn-ing the bus-y peo-ple, Far and near!___

How many measures are like the measures marked ⌐▢⌐ ?
Find some other measures that are alike.

Some Day

Adapted Words   Bohemian Folk Tune

1. Some day I will be a cow-boy rid-ing on the plain,

Driv-ing herds of Tex-as cat-tle through the wind and rain;

With my las-so I will rope an-y do-gie on the lope;

Some day I will be a cow-boy rid-ing on the plain.

2. Some day I will be a flyer riding in the sky,
Piloting a silver jet, into space I'll fly;
I will fly up to the moon, take a look and come back soon;
Some day I will be a flyer riding in the sky.

3. Some day I will be a fireman riding on a truck,
Racing to a burning building takes a lot of pluck;
I will climb a ladder high, pour the water on the fire;
Some day I will be a fireman riding on a truck.

I'm a Goose

The goose wiped her eyes on a towel
And sobbed, "I'm as wise as the owl.
    But what is the use?
    Just because I'm a goose
They say I'm a silly old fowl."

—Elizabeth Newell

Peek-a-Boo Kangaroo

Said little Baby Kangaroo,
    "It's wonderful to see
How Mother hops and jumps along
    With a pocketful of ME!"

—Mabel Watts

Make up your own melodies for these two poems.

121

Get on Board

Negro Folk Song

WELL ACCENTED

Refrain

Get on board, lit - tle chil-dren, Get on board, lit - tle chil-dren,

End

Get on board, lit - tle chil-dren, There's room for man-y a more!

Leader   SLOWER, IN FREE RHYTHM

1. The lit - tle black train's a - com-ing, I hear it round the bend,—

in time   Go to the beginning.

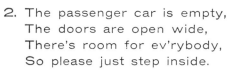

I hear the big wheels rum-bling And roll-ing through the land.

2. The passenger car is empty,
   The doors are open wide,
   There's room for ev'rybody,
   So please just step inside.

3. The little black train's a long train,
   A fast train, you will find;
   The red caboose is coming,
   It's tagging on behind.

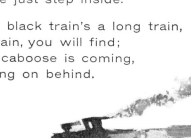

122

so do re mi fa so
5 1 2 3 4 5

Money Makes the Mare to Go (6-tone song) Adapted American Song

FAST

1. Mon-ey makes the mare to go wheth-er she has legs or no,
2. My old mare, she would not go till I got the mon-ey, O,

Mon-ey makes the mare to go wheth-er she has legs or no,
My old mare, she would not go till I got the mon-ey, O,

Au-tumn, win-ter, sum-mer, O, nev-er mind, she's sure to go,
Then the corn, it made her go, and she got quite frisk-y, O,

Au-tumn, win-ter, sum-mer, O, nev-er mind, she's sure to go.
Then the corn, it made her go, and she got quite frisk-y, O.

In a Supersonic Jet

Words and Music by Richard C. Berg

With a might-y roar___ at the take-off,___

Sil-ver jets are tak-ing to the sky;

Fast-er than sound they trav-el,_ Look quick! They're pass-ing by.

I think some day I'll be a pi-lot

And go streak-ing by at su-per-son-ic speed

On my way to new and dis-tant plac-es.

In a jet, (whoosh) yes, a jet, (whoosh)

Way up high in a jet I will fly.

Down the River

American Play Party Song

1,2,3. The riv - er is up, and the chan-nel is deep,

The wind is stead - y and strong.—

1. Oh, won't we have a jol - ly good time
2. Oh, Di - nah, put the hoe - cake on
3. The waves do splash from shore— to shore

126

1,2,3. As we go sail - ing a - long.

Down the riv - er, oh, down the riv - er,

Oh, down the riv - er we go - o - o!

Down the riv - er, oh, down the riv - er,

Oh, down the O - hi - o!_____

Home on the Range

Cowboy Song

1. Oh, give me a home where the buf - fa - lo roam,
2. How of - ten at night, when the heav - ens are bright,

Where the deer and the an - te - lope play, _____
With the light from the glit - ter - ing stars, _____

Where __ sel - dom is heard a dis - cour - ag - ing word,
Have I stood there a - mazed and __ asked as I gazed,

And the skies are not cloud - y all day. _____
If their glo - ry ex - ceeds that of ours. _____

Home, home on the range,—Where the deer and the an-te-lope play,—

Where sel-dom is heard a dis-cour-ag-ing word,

And the skies are not cloud-y all day.———

Beat this rhythm steadily throughout, with a wood block or paper cups: $\frac{4}{4}$ ♩ ♩ ♩ ♩

Branding Song

Words and Music by Daniel Hooley

STURDILY

Throw a las-so! Yup! You got him!

Pull it tight! Pull it tight! Pull it tight!

Are the brand-ing irons— read-y?

We've got to brand all the steers by to-night.

So throw your las-so out a-gain,

130

Just as you did be-fore;

We've got to rope a thou-sand head

And brand a thou-sand more.

Go to the beginning.

◗ Leader of the Band

Words and Music by Stephen Scott

1., 2. I'd like to be the lead - er of a band!

I'd like to stand up in front and wave my hand!

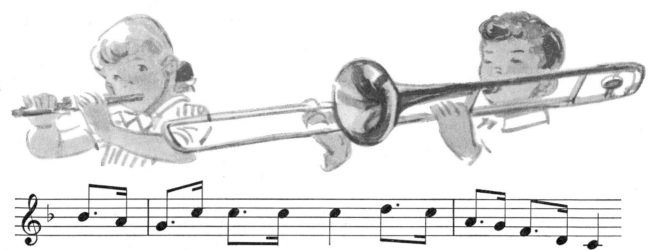

1. First I'd have the trum-pets blare while the pic-co-lo would toot,
2. Next I'd have the snare drums roll while the clar-i-net would sing,

Then I'd bring in the trom-bones and the sil-ver flute.
Then I'd bring in the cym-bals with a zing zing zing!

1., 2. I'd like to be the lead-er of a band,

The lead-er of a con-cert band.
march-ing

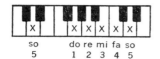

The Shangri-la Conductor (6-tone song)

Southern Folk Song

One Child: 1. I am a good con-duc-tor, I live in Shan-gri - la!

Class: He is a good con-duc-tor, he lives in Shan-gri - la!

Child: I can play my Class: He can play his

Child: Vi - o, vi - o, vi - o - la, vi - o - la, vi - o - la,

Class: Vi - o, vi - o, vi - o - la, vi - o, vi - o - la.

2. I am a good conductor, I live in Shangri-la!
   He is a good conductor, he lives in Shangri-la!
   I can play my, He can play his
   Oompah, oompah, big bass drum, big bass drum, big bass drum,
   Oompah, oompah, big bass drum, oompah, big bass drum.

3. I am a good conductor, I live in Shangri-la!
   He is a good conductor, he lives in Shangri-la!
   I can play my, He can play his
   Ta ta ta ta, xylophone, xylophone, xylophone,
   Ta ta ta ta, xylophone, ta ta, xylophone.

4. I am a good conductor, I live in Shangri-la!
   He is a good conductor, he lives in Shangri-la!
   I can play my, He can play his
   Too too too too, little flute, little flute, little flute,
   Too too too too, little flute, too too, little flute.

   Sing about some other instruments.

135

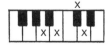

4 tones

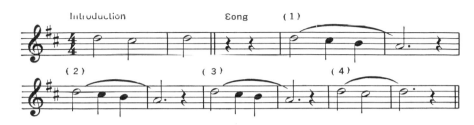

The Music Box

Words by F. Winthrop   French Tune

LIGHTLY

1. Now the mu - sic box will play,
2. Grand-ma says it came from France,

Grand-ma took the key— and— wound it;
That is where she says— she— found it;

All its tunes are bright and gay,
Hear this queer old - fash - ioned dance,

Though they most - ly sound— the— same.
"Am - a - ryl - lis" is— its— name.

Edward MacDowell was an American. He liked to be outdoors, and he wrote music about flowers, trees, the wind, and other outdoor things. He wrote "Of Br'er Rabbit."

Br'er Rabbit was a happy little bunny that played in the woods with the other animals. The tune that starts the piece is a happy up-and-down tune. You will hear it more times as the piece is played.

Of Br'er Rabbit

Music by Edward Mac Dowell

Here is a waltz. It was written by Johannes Brahms, who lived in Vienna many years ago. He wrote much music that people like to hear and play. Hum the piece when you hear it played.

Waltz

Op. 39, No. 15

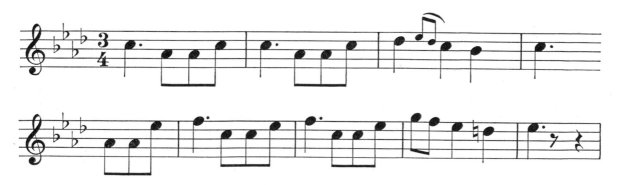

137

◑ Day (Coppelia Waltz)

Adapted Words   Music by Leo Delibes

In the air o - ver - head, There's a flut - ter of wings;

From the top of the tree, a gay mock-ing bird sings.

Can you tell why he's gay? Do you know that the day

Has be - gun, Night is done. Here's the sun! ___

Leo Delibes was a French composer who wrote many fine dances.

When Johann Sebastian Bach was a little boy in Germany, many, many years ago, he wanted to write music. His grandfather, uncles, and brothers all wrote music. So he worked hard in music all his life. Now, a long time after he lived, some of the most beautiful music that we hear is the music of Bach.

Minuet

Viennese Musical Clock

Adapted Words   Music by Zoltán Kodály

Hear the beat - ing drum!

Oh, here the sol - diers come!

They step a - round and round in the tow'r

To tell each one the hour.

This piece is about a clock in the tower of a king's palace. Every time the clock sounded the hour, it would play a tune. Then toy soldiers would step around and around in the tower, keeping time to the music.

140

Early One Morning

English Folk Song

HAPPILY

1. Ear - ly one morn - ing, be - fore the sun had ris - en,
2. One Au-tumn aft - er-noon, just as the sun was set - ting,

I heard a blue-bird in the fields— gai - ly sing:
I heard a blue-bird in a tree— pipe a song:

softly

"South winds are blow - ing, green grass is grow - ing,
"Fare - well, we're go - ing, cold winds are blow - ing,

louder

We— come to tell you of the mer - ry— spring."
But— we'll be back— when the days— grow— long."

141

Winter and Summer

Words by H. O. Knowlton   Music by N. H. Allen

SMOOTHLY, IN SWINGING RHYTHM

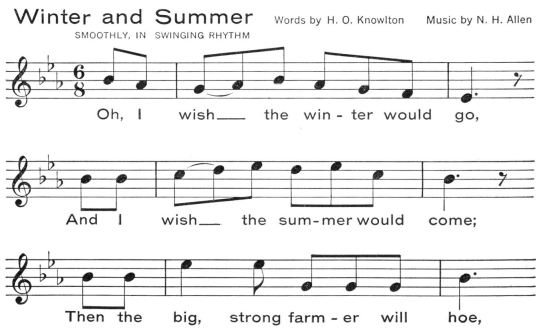

Oh, I wish___ the win - ter would go,

And I wish___ the sum - mer would come;

Then the big, strong farm - er will hoe,

And the lit - tle brown bee will hum,_mm-m.

Oh, the blos-soms take long— to come,

And the i - ci - cles long— to go;

But the sum-mer will come, and the bees will hum,

And the bright lit - tle brook_ will flow, I know,

And the bright lit - tle brook will flow, mm - m.

Redbird in Spring

Adapted Words   Slovak Folk Tune

LIGHTLY

1. In our cher-ry tree I hear a red - bird sing,
2. Lit - tle bird, I like your hap-py spring -time song;

Sing a hap - py mel - o - dy a - bout the spring,
Win-ter's o - ver, spring is here, and days grow long;

Sing of spring - time flow - ers,
Sing of sun - ny weath - er,

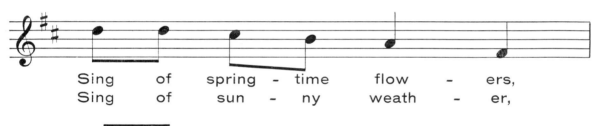

Sing of A - pril show - ers;
Count your joys to - geth - er;

In our cher-ry tree I hear a red - bird sing.
Lit - tle bird, I like your hap - py spring -time song.

do mi so so
1 3 5 5

My Kite

SMOOTHLY

Words by H. W. Loomis   Music by A. E. Johnstone

Skipwise

G   G   C   C   G   D7

1. How high my kite can fly in the breez-es of A-pril!
2. My kite is gay and bright as the flow-ers of A-pril,

G   G   C   A min.   D7   G

It sails a-round the sky where it pleas-es, in A-pril.
But such a sor-ry sight in the show-ers of A-pril!

Make up a good tune for this spring song:

When Blue Sky Smiles

When blue sky smiles and birds come back
And little flowers are springing,
I feel inside all shiny warm,
Like dancing and like singing.

—Olive Beaupre Miller

145

so do re mi fa so
5 1 2 3 4 5

My Tree House (6 - tone song)

Adapted Words   Czech Folk Tune

WELL ACCENTED

1. Out in the ap - ple tree in our back - yard,
2. Birds come and sing me a greet-ing up there;

High up we built a tree house;
"Chee - ree!" means "How do you do?"

House in the tree, Made just for me;
Rob - in, hel - lo! Rob - in, don't go!

Come out and see, You will a - gree
Swing to and fro, Look down be - low,

146

Noth-ing is fin - er than play - ing up there,
See how the wind rus -tles leaves a - round me,

High up a - mong the green boughs.
High up in my own tree house.

147

so fa mi re do
5   4   3   2   1

4
fa
X

do re mi   so
1   2   3   5

Easter

Music by Robert Williams (1817)

1. Now the earth is green a - gain,
2. Daf - fo - dils a - gain are_here,

Bells play

Sing we now al - le - lu - ia!
Sing we now al - le - lu - ia!

Rob - ins sing their songs a - gain,
Best of times in all the_year,

Bells play

Sing we now al - le - lu - ia!
Sing we now al - le - lu - ia!

148

Easter Time

Words by Mary Owen Bruce   Music by Daniel Hooley

GAILY

1. East-er is a mer-ry time, A mer-ry, mer-ry, cheer-y time,

Ba-by chicks come pop-ping out, East-er bun-nies flop a-bout;

Oh, East-er _____ is a mer-ry time. _____

2. Easter is a new, new time,
   A spicky, spanky brand new time,
   Easter hats and socks and shoes,
   Shirts and ties, to name a few;
   Oh, Easter is a new, new time.

3. Easter is a bright, gay time,
   An Easter-hunt-and-party time,
   Eggs of green and red and blue,
   Choc'late ones for you and you;
   Oh, Easter is a bright, gay time.

149

Miss Breeze

Words and Music by Daniel Protheroe

LIGHTLY

1. I know a young la - dy who lives in the sky;
2. I've heard her at chim-neys and win-dows and doors;

You__ nev - er could see her, al-though you might try;
She's_ al - ways a - bout when a thun - der-storm roars;

She shouts on the shore and laughs on the seas;
She push-es the waves and jog-gles the trees;

Per - haps you have guessed, she is Miss A - pril Breeze.
A mis-chie-vous girl is__ Miss A - pril Breeze.

What phrases are skipwise?

What phrases are stepwise?

🎵 The Woodpecker

Adapted Words   French Folk Tune

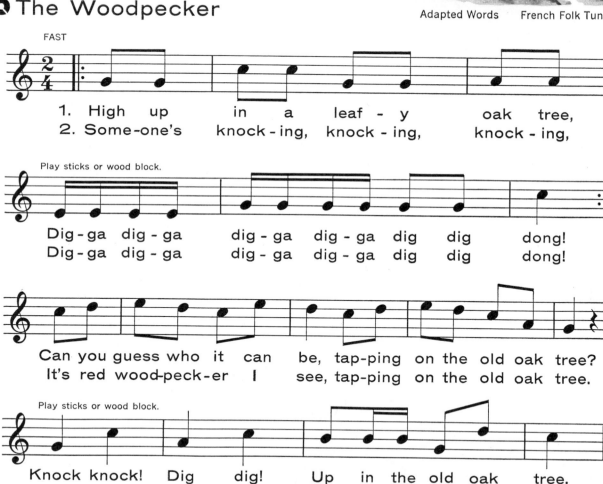

FAST

1. High up   in a   leaf - y   oak   tree,
2. Some-one's   knock - ing,   knock - ing,   knock - ing,

Play sticks or wood block.

Dig - ga dig - ga   dig - ga dig - ga dig   dig   dong!
Dig - ga dig - ga   dig - ga dig - ga dig   dig   dong!

Can you guess who it can   be, tap-ping on the old oak tree?
It's red wood-peck-er I   see, tap-ping on the old oak tree.

Play sticks or wood block.

Knock knock! Dig   dig!   Up   in the old oak   tree.
Knock knock! Dig   dig!   Up   in the old oak   tree.

151

Stand and make big arm-swings to the music.

On Wheels

Words and Music by Richard C. Berg

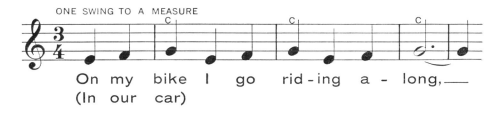

ONE SWING TO A MEASURE

On my bike I go rid-ing a - long,——
(In our car)

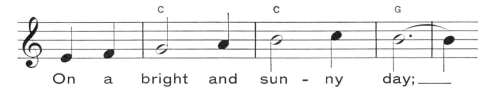

On a bright and sun - ny day;——

As I ride, I like hum-ming the sound—

Of the wheels as they go 'round.——

152

(Hum) _____

Hum-ming a tune, a bi-cy-cle tune
(mo - tor - car)

With - out a sin - gle care; ___

On my bike I go rid-ing a - long ___
(In our car)

In the bright and sun - ny air. ___

What phrases sound alike?

Coming on a Rainbow

Adapted Words   Negro Melody

WITH GOOD ACCENT

Class: Com-ing on a rain-bow, Com-ing on a cloud,

Com-ing to the earth by and by;

I'm a-com-ing on a rain-bow, Com-ing on a cloud,

Com-ing to the earth by and by.

Child: I'm a-com-ing on the breez-es, Com-ing to the earth,

Class: Com - ing to the earth by and by;

Child: I'm a - slid-ing on a moon-beam, Com-ing to the earth,

Go to the beginning.

Class: Com-ing to the earth by and by.

When you sing the song again, you can sing "dancing" instead of "coming." Or you can sing "flying" or "hopping."

Spring in China

Cantonese Folk Song

SMOOTHLY, FLOWINGLY

Spring paints the blue— sky with clouds of— white;

Spring paints the green grass with flow - ers— bright;

Spring brings song-birds from far a - way,

Hap - py mu - sic they sing all— day.

Spring-time is col - or - ful, bright and— gay.

Play all through the song: 4 Drum
4

Shakers

Sticks

Gong

In China

Adapted Words   Chinese Folk Tune

WELL ACCENTED

Tching-a ring-a ring is a tune peo-ple sing,

This is what they sing in Chi-na, o-ver the sea.

Cym-bals are clang-ing with a cling ting-a ting!

Tching-a ring-a ring! In Chi-na.

The Wren and the Hen <small>Traditional Words · Music by Daniel Hooley</small>

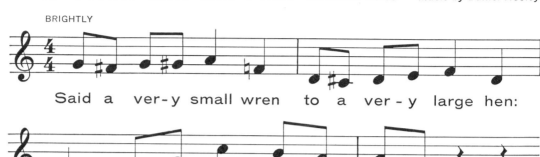

Said a ver-y small wren to a ver-y large hen:

"Why do you make such a clat-ter?

For who ev-er could guess that an egg, more or less,

Should be thought so im-por-tant a mat-ter?"

Then an-swered the hen to the ver-y lit-tle wren:

"If I laid ti-ny eggs like you, mad-am,

I would not cluck so loud, nor feel ver-y proud;

Look at these, how you'd crow if you had them!"

Garden in the Sea

Adapted Words   German Folk Tune

SLOWLY

1. Oh, I   won-der if you   know
2. All   the   flow-ers float-ing   there

There's a   place where flow-ers   grow,
Are   as   beau - ti - ful and   fair

Where the   sun - light nev - er   shines,
As   the   ros - es   of   the   spring

And sum-mer breez - es   nev - er   blow;
That show-er   per-fume   on   the   air;

It's   a   gar - den   in   the   deep,
And   the   flow - ers   of   the   sea,

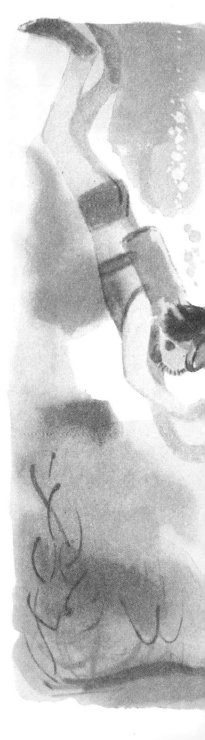

It's a place that mer-maids keep
Grow-ing love - ly, bloom - ing free,

In the caves be-neath the o - cean,
Glow in col - ors of the rain-bow

Where the shad-ows ev - er sleep.
In the gar-den of the sea.

161

The Fog

Words by A. Vance   Music by Eleanor Smith

SMOOTHLY

1. It drift-ed in so cool and white,
2. And cling-ing there to leaf and flow'rs,

It rest-ed on the shore,
A wea-ry ghost it lay,

It float-ed in a hun-dred shapes
But when the morn-ing sun-shine came,

I'd nev-er seen be-fore.
It soft-ly crept a-way.

162

Swimming Time

Words by Susan Rupert   Music by Daniel Hooley

Child: 1. When sum-mer comes, I'll swim in the pool,
     2. When fall comes 'round, I'll go for a hike,

Swim in the wa-ter so fresh and so cool.
Play out of doors, and then ride on my bike.

Refrain

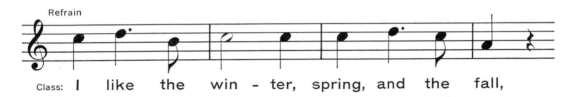

Class: I like the win-ter, spring, and the fall,

But swim-ming time, sum-mer time I like best of all.

3. When winter comes, with winds blowing chill,
   Skating is fun; so is coasting down hill.

4. When springtime comes, with sunshine and show'rs,
   I'll make a garden and tend to my flow'rs.

After each stanza, sing the Refrain.

163

Good King Henry
Traditional Words   Music by Daniel Hooley

When good King Hen - ry went to sea,

Ev - 'ry ship__ had sail - ors three,

One to steer and one to row,

And one to watch_ the wild wind blow!

And one to watch_ the wild wind blow!__

The ship went up, the ship went down,

The King leaned o-ver and lost his crown!

"Dear, oh, dear!" King Hen - ry said,

"To think of my crown on a fish - 's head!

To think of my crown on a fish - 's head!"

The Question

Adapted Words   Music by Franz Schubert

I   can-not ask   the   flow'rs,_   Nor   all   the stars that   glow,_

For   none of them ev - er can tell me What   I should like to know;

And yet   I think that some-where There's some-one who would know _

Just where all the breez-es come from, And where the breez-es go!

166

Baby Birds

Paraphrase   French Folk Song

WITH EXPRESSION

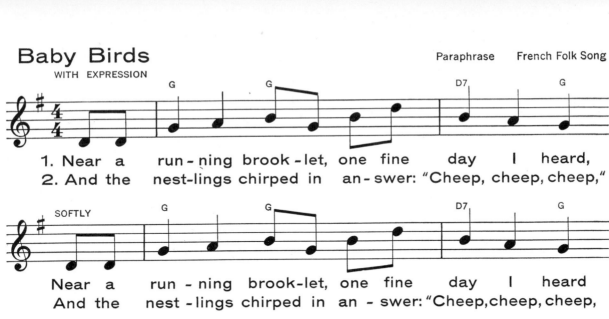

1. Near a run-ning brook-let, one fine day I heard,
2. And the nest-lings chirped in an-swer: "Cheep, cheep, cheep,"

Near a run-ning brook-let, one fine day I heard
And the nest-lings chirped in an-swer: "Cheep, cheep, cheep,

Moth-er bird sing to her nest-lings,
Let us sing just like our moth-er!"

Moth-er bird sing to her nest-lings,
So they sang just like their moth-er:

I ____ heard her sing, I ____ heard her sing.
"Cheep, cheep, cheep!" they sang, "Cheep, cheep, cheep!" they sang.

Listen to the Mocking Bird

Adapted Words   Music by Alice Hawthorne

The mock-ing bird in the chi-na-ber-ry tree,

In the chi-na-ber-ry tree, in the chi-na-ber-ry tree,

The mock-ing bird in the chi-na-ber-ry tree

Is sing-ing all the songs he knows for me.

Lis-ten to the mock-ing bird, (bell)

Lis-ten to the mock-ing bird, (bell)

The mock-ing bird is sing-ing in the tree, (bell)

Lis-ten to the mock-ing bird, (bell)

Lis-ten to the mock-ing bird, (bell)

He's sing-ing all the songs he knows for me.

Hearing

Words by Florence C. Fox   Music by W. Otto Miessner

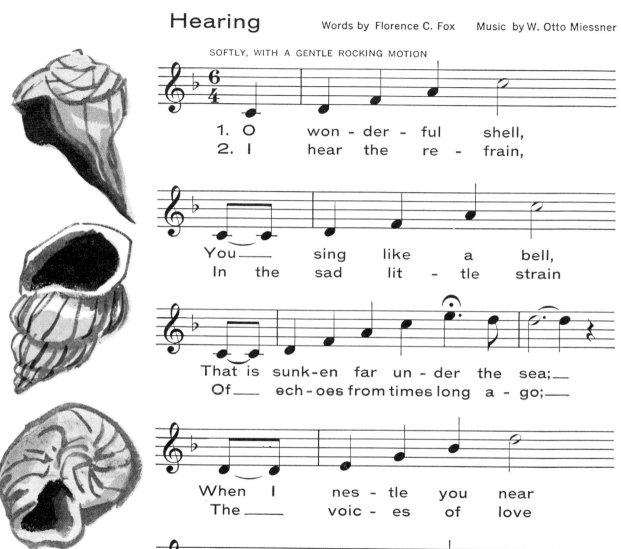

SOFTLY, WITH A GENTLE ROCKING MOTION

1. O   won - der - ful   shell,
2. I   hear the   re - frain,

You___   sing   like   a   bell,
In   the   sad   lit - tle   strain

That is sunk-en far un - der the sea;___
Of___ ech - oes from times long a - go;___

When   I   nes - tle   you   near
The ___   voic - es   of   love

To   my   list' - ning   ear,
That ___   call   from   a - bove

You   whis - per sweet mu - sic to   me.___
Or   mur - mur where deep wa - ters flow.___

Whis - per,   whis - per,   Whis-per sweet mu-sic to me,___
Mur - mur,   mur - mur,   Mur-mur where deep wa-ters flow,___

Whis - per,   whis - per,   Whis-per sweet mu-sic to me.___
Mur - mur,   mur - mur,   Mur-mur where deep wa-ters flow.___

From ART SONG CYCLES by W. Otto Miessner and Florence C. Fox, ©1910, 1938, Silver Burdett Company.

CINDERELLA
A Song Story

Once upon a time, in a country far away, there lived a good little girl named Cinderella. She had a bad stepmother and two stepsisters who made her work very hard. They never sang. They never smiled, and so they were not pretty to look at. They were ugly.

❶ They Look Ugly

WELL ACCENTED

They look ug - ly and cross, all their smiles they have lost,

They are ug - ly! Oh, so ug - ly!

All their thoughts are un - kind, it's no won-der to find

That they're ug - ly! Oh, so ug - ly!

They are mean, mean, mean. You've nev-er seen, seen, seen

An - y three so mean in all your life._____

These three women were as mean as they could be to Cinderella. They would keep her busy all day, cleaning house, washing clothes, and waiting on them. They thought it was funny to make her do things over and over again. She never had time to sing or play or dance. She had to work all the time.

Cinderella!

1. Cin-der-el-la! Cin-der-el-la! Cin-der-el-la,
2. Cin-der-el-la! Cin-der-el-la! Cin-der-el-la,

sweep the floor! Cin-der-el-la! Cin-der-el-la!
scrub the floor! Cin-der-el-la! Cin-der-el-la!

When you've swept it, sweep it some more. Ha ha ha ha!
When you've scrubbed it, scrub it some more. Ha ha ha ha!

Sweep it some more. Ha ha ha ha! Sweep it some more.—
Scrub it some more. Ha ha ha ha! Scrub it some more.—

When Cinderella was through with her work in the house,
she had to help her ugly sisters dress for parties and balls.
One day, she helped them dress for a ball that was being
given for the King's son, the Prince.

174

Fetch My Shawl

HURRIEDLY

Cin-der-el-la, fetch my shawl! Cin-der-el-la, fetch my fan!
Cin-der-el-la, fetch my shoe! Cin-der-el-la, fetch my lace!

Cin-der-el-la, fetch my gloves! Try to hur-ry, if you can.
Cin-der-el-la, fetch my hat! And some pow-der for my face.

Cin-der-el-la, hur-ry up! Cin-der-el-la, don't be slow!

The ball is at the pal-ace, and it's time to go.

When Cinderella saw their beautiful dresses, and when she
thought of the good time they would have at the ball, she said:

◐ I Would Like to Go!

SIMPLY

Cinderella: "I would like to go to the ball!"

Sisters: "Don't be sil - ly, you can't go at all!

She would like to go to the ball!

Who would want to have her at the ball?

Her at the ball! Who would want to have her at the ball?"

Cinderella was very unhappy. When her sisters had gone
to the ball, she sat in her little chair by the fireside and cried
until she went to sleep.

Then a wonderful thing happened! There was her Fairy Godmother standing before her! She waved her wand, and lo and behold! Cinderella had on a beautiful dress! On her feet were pretty slippers made of glass!

The Fairy Godmother waved her wand again, and lo and behold! A pumpkin and six mice became a wonderful coach pulled by six proud horses!

"You may go to the ball now," said the Fairy Godmother. "But you must be sure to leave the ball before the clock strikes twelve."

So Cinderella went to the ball in her beautiful dress and pretty slippers made of glass, in her wonderful coach pulled by six proud horses. When the Prince saw Cinderella, he asked her to waltz with him.

Waltzing

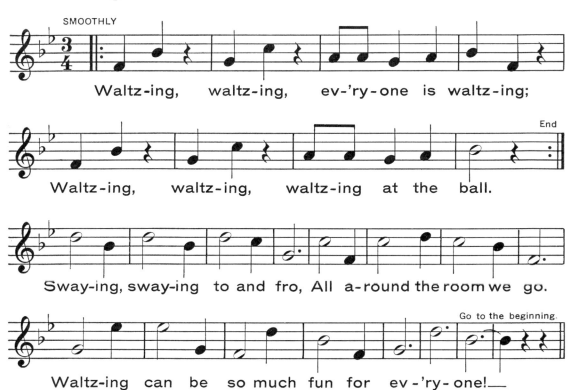

Waltz-ing, waltz-ing, ev-'ry-one is waltz-ing;

Waltz-ing, waltz-ing, waltz-ing at the ball.

Sway-ing, sway-ing to and fro, All a-round the room we go.

Waltz-ing can be so much fun for ev-'ry-one!

Cinderella and the Prince danced and danced. All at once the clock began to strike twelve! Cinderella knew she must leave right away. She ran from the palace, but in her hurry she lost one of her pretty slippers made of glass. The Prince found it on the steps and told his father, the King, that he wanted to find the beautiful girl who had lost it.

So the very next day, the King sent out the Prince and his messengers to find her. They went from house to house, looking for her. At last they came to the home of Cinderella and her ugly sisters.

❂The Messengers

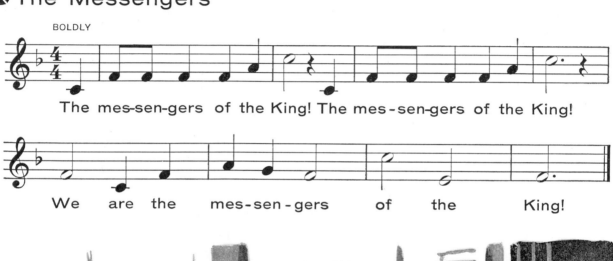

The mes-sen-gers of the King! The mes-sen-gers of the King!

We are the mes-sen-gers of the King!

Then the messengers of the King read a royal proclamation:

♦ A Royal Proclamation

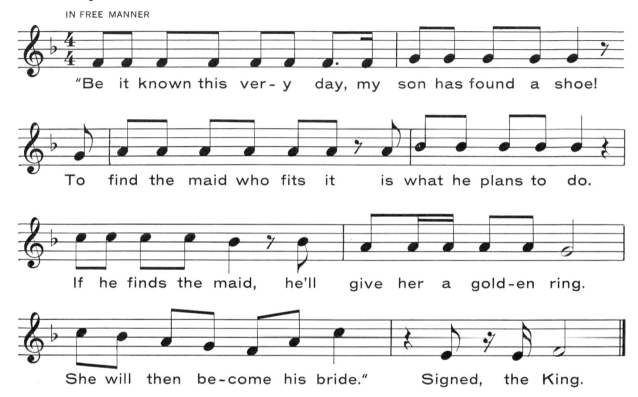

IN FREE MANNER

"Be it known this ver-y day, my son has found a shoe!

To find the maid who fits it is what he plans to do.

If he finds the maid, he'll give her a gold-en ring.

She will then be-come his bride." Signed, the King.

The ugly stepmother wanted the ugly sisters to try on the slipper made of glass. She sang:

♦ Try On the Shoe!

"Try on the shoe, for it might fit you!

180

Try on the shoe! It might be yours."

First one sister and then the other sister tried and tried to put on the slipper. They could not. Their feet were too big.

Then the Prince said to Cinderella, "Why don't you try on the slipper?"

Everyone laughed and made fun of her. But Cinderella, sat down and tried on the slipper.

"Try on the shoe, oh, Cin-der-el-la!

Try on the shoe! It might fit you.

Look! Look! Cin-der-el-la's foot fit's the shoe!—

♦ Marry the Prince!

HAPPILY

Cin - der - el - la will mar-ry the Prince,

Mar-ry the Prince, mar-ry the Prince!

Cin - der - el - la will mar-ry the Prince,

Mar - ry the Prince!

182

And, of course, that is just what happened. Cinderella married the Prince. Now she knew that if the ugly sisters could only learn to smile, they would not be ugly any more. They would be as happy as she was. So everyone in the palace sang:

Try a Great Big Smile!

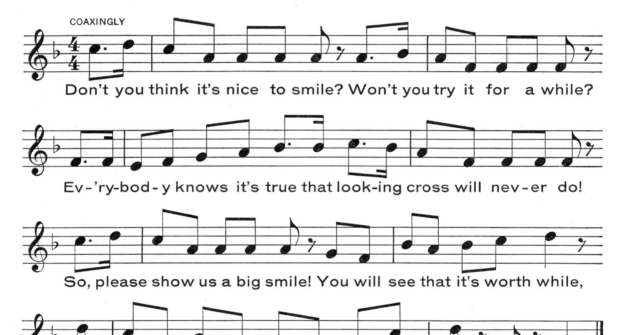

Don't you think it's nice to smile? Won't you try it for a while?

Ev-'ry-bod-y knows it's true that look-ing cross will nev-er do!

So, please show us a big smile! You will see that it's worth while,

Come on, you ug-ly sis-ters, try a great big smile!

When, at last, the ugly sisters learned to smile, everyone was surprised to see how beautiful they were. The Prince's two brothers fell in love with them and married them. The King gave another ball. Everyone smiled and was happy. Everyone danced and sang "Waltzing" again.

● Tiny Town Bells A Song Story by Daniel Hooley

Once upon a time there was a tiny town that owned
a wonderful set of magic bells. When things were going
well, the bells would ring every hour, day or night, like this:

SMOOTHLY

Ding-ding - a - dong! Ding-ding-a - dong!

Then everyone knew that the bells were saying:

Ev -'ry-thing's fine, That I can tell;
Ev -'ry-thing's fine, Ding-ding-dong bell!

Now it so happened, one day, that the people of the town woke up to hear the bells ringing like this:

EXCITEDLY

Ding - a - ding-dong; ding - a - ding-dong;

Ding - a - ding - ding - dong!

Everyone knew that the bells were saying:

EXCITEDLY

Some - thing's hap - pened,

some - thing's hap - pened,

Some - thing you won't like.

185

So they all ran into the streets in nightgowns and nightcaps to see what was the matter. They said to one another:

MODERATELY

What can the mat-ter be? What can the mat-ter be?

Why do the bells all ring that way?

Is there a fire? We can't see it!

Is there an-y smoke? We can't smell it!

Are the cows and sheep all loose?

Go to the beginning.

Noth-ing's miss-ing but the old gray goose.

All the people went back to their homes to dress properly. Then the boys and girls went to the baker to get fresh bread and rolls for breakfast.

WITH A SWING

Go - ing to the bak-er-y store,

bak-er - y store, bak-er - y store,

Go -ing to the bak-er - y store to

buy some bread for break-fast.___

All at once, everyone said, "Oh, look!"

MODERATELY

The bak-er-y shop is closed; The win-dow blinds are drawn;

The bak-er-y door is locked; The bak-er must not be in town.

End

What shall we do for bread? What shall we do for buns?

Go to the beginning.

What shall we do for bread to eat un-til the bak-er comes?

Then the bells began to ring again:

EXCITEDLY

1. Ding - a - ding - dong,
2. Some-thing's hap - pened,

ding - a - ding - dong;
some-thing's hap - pened,

Ding - a - ding - ding - dong!
Some-thing you don't like.

So the boys and girls went home sadly, and as they went they sang:

SLOWLY

No bread! No rolls! Oh, un - hap - py day!

No bread for break-fast! What will Moth-er say?

Just then the Old Red Rooster came running down the street, saying:

RATHER FAST

Gra - cious! Mer - cy!

What a sleep - y head!

I did - n't crow this morn - ing,

So the bak - er's still in bed.

So the children answered:

HAPPILY

Let's wake the bak-er up, Let's get him out of bed!
Let's wake the bak-er up, So he can bake some bread.

Then the rooster crowed:

Cock - a - doo - dle - doo, Cock - a - doo - dle - doo,

Cock - a - doo - dle doo - dle doo - dle doo!

That woke the baker up. He began to bake the bread, and the town bells rang:

SMOOTHLY

Ding-ding - a - dong! Ding-ding - a - dong!

And everyone knew that the bells were saying:

Ev -'ry-thing's fine, That I can tell;
Ev -'ry-thing's fine, Ding-ding-dong bell!

191

Sectional Index of Recordings

One album of two LP recordings: four sides (J07P—0509, 0510, 0511, 0512)
Produced by Audio Education, Inc., distributed by American Book Company

Alphabetical Index of Recordings

CLASSIFIED INDEX

ALPHABETICAL INDEX OF SONGS